The Open University

M248 Analysing data

Computer Book A

About M248

This computer book forms part of the module M248 *Analysing data*. M248 uses two software packages, including *MINITAB for Windows* (Minitab Inc.), to explore and analyse data and to investigate statistical concepts. The software packages are provided as part of the module. Their use is covered in the four computer books, of which this is one. This computer book covers all the computer work associated with Block A.

The Open University, Walton Hall, Milton Keynes, MK7 6AA.

First published 2003. Second edition 2009. Third edition 2012.

Edited, designed and typeset by The Open University, using the Open University TEX System.

Printed in the United Kingdom by Hobbs the Printers Limited, Brunel Road, Totton, Hampshire SO40 3WX.

ISBN 978 1 8487 3632 0

3.1

Contents

Introduction

This computer book covers all the computer work associated with Block A of *M248 Analysing data*.

Using this book

As you study each unit in Block A you will be directed to work through particular chapters in this book as part of your work on that unit. Each unit contains instructions as to when you should first refer to particular material in this computer book, so you are advised not to work on the activities here until you have reached the appropriate points in the units. You will be asked to study Chapter 6 as part of your work on the first tutor-marked assignment (TMA).

The activities vary in nature and length. Some contain instructions on how to use the software to perform particular tasks; and some suggest ways in which you can use the software to investigate statistical ideas or to help you to develop your understanding of concepts. Others provide practice at using the software to explore or analyse data; you will find solutions to these activities at the end of the computer book. You should try to work through all the computer activities as you read the chapters.

A few supplementary computer exercises on the whole of Block A are provided after Chapter 14. You may use these for extra practice or for revision (or not at all), as you wish.

Conventions used in the computer books

For clarity of presentation, bold-face type has been used for file names in the computer books. The names of menus and items in menus are also printed in bold-face type when referred to in the text, as are options and the names of fields and buttons in dialogue boxes.

When you are asked to use the mouse to click on an item, you should assume that this refers to the left-hand mouse button. Where you need to use the right-hand mouse button this will be stated explicitly.

About the software

The software for M248 has two components: MINITAB and SUStats (Software for Understanding Statistics). MINITAB is a data analysis package; it is introduced in Chapter 1 and is used throughout M248. SUStats consists of programs designed specifically to help develop your understanding and appreciation of certain statistical concepts. The first four programs are used in Chapter 7 and are associated with ideas introduced in *Unit A3*. The software is contained on the CD-ROM labelled *M248 Analysing data*.

See the M248 website for information on the software supplied, including the release number of the version of MINITAB that you should have received.

Chapter 1
Introducing MINITAB

In this chapter, the data analysis software package MINITAB is introduced. If you have not yet installed the M248 software on your computer, then do so now. Instructions are given in the *Software Guide*.

The MINITAB environment is discussed briefly in Section 1.1. You will learn how to produce a pie chart in Section 1.2, and how to save your work in Section 1.3. In Section 1.4, a useful feature called the *Project Manager* is described. The remaining sections describe how to print output and how to paste output into a word-processor document.

1.1 Getting started

Computer Activity 1.1   Running MINITAB

Run MINITAB now: double-click on the MINITAB icon on your desktop.

You will see briefly an information panel telling you which version of MINITAB is being used. Following this, you should see the opening screen as shown in Figure 1.1.

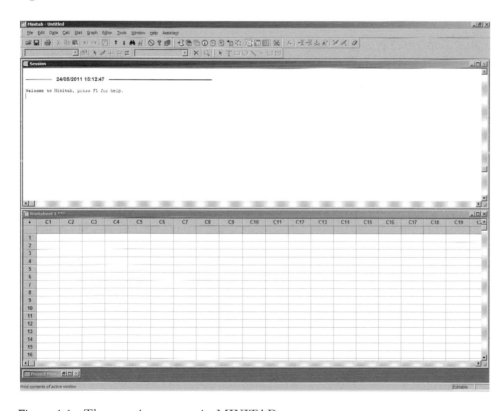

Figure 1.1   The opening screen in MINITAB

The form of the opening screen is similar to that of many Windows-based software packages: there is a menu bar at the top of the screen and a status bar along the bottom. For MINITAB, there are two windows between these—the top window is called the *Session* window and the bottom one is the *Data* window. Roughly speaking, the Session window is where your results are displayed and the Data window displays your data. One other window is present at all times, the *Project Manager* window, but this is minimized on the opening screen (near the bottom of the screen). The Project Manager window will be discussed in Section 1.4.

Click on **File** in the menu bar to view the contents of the **File** menu. Notice that, as you move the mouse pointer down the menu, the status bar provides information about each item. An arrowhead pointing to the right on a menu item indicates the existence of a submenu. If you click on **File** again, the menu will close.

Before moving on to the next activity, spend a few minutes exploring the menus and their submenus. Note the different types of facilities available in the different menus.

By the way, you can exit from MINITAB at any time, simply by clicking on **File** and choosing **Exit** (by clicking on it).

Comment

The roles of the menus may be broadly summarized as follows. The **File** and **Edit** menus contain commands for handling and editing files. The **Data** menu allows you to manipulate data in the Data window. Calculations are carried out using the **Calc** menu and statistical techniques are available using the **Stat** menu. The **Graph** menu is used to create graphs and diagrams. Some types of window may be edited using the **Editor** menu. The **Tools** menu allows access to other facilities such as *Microsoft Calculator*, *Notepad* and *Windows Explorer* from within MINITAB. It can also be used to customize the MINITAB menus and submenus. As for other Windows-based software packages, the **Window** menu is for rearranging windows or activating a specified window and the **Help** menu provides access to online help. The **Assistant** menu includes help with choosing appropriate techniques for analysing and displaying data.

Computer Activity 1.2   Opening a MINITAB worksheet ──────────

In MINITAB, data are stored in *worksheets*. Although worksheets are not themselves visible, when a worksheet is opened the data it contains are displayed in a Data window. All the worksheets for M248 are located in the **M248 Data Files** folder within **My Documents** (or **Documents**).

The data described in Example 1.7 of *Unit A1* on the surgical removal of tattoos are contained in a worksheet named **tattoos.mtw**. Open this worksheet, as follows.

◇   Click on **File**, then choose **Open Worksheet...** from the menu (by clicking on it). The **Open Worksheet** dialogue box will open.

> Notice that the file name extension of a MINITAB worksheet is **mtw**.

Navigate to the folder where the M248 worksheets are stored, as follows.

◇   For Windows 7, the list of folders in **My Documents** will be displayed in the main panel.

◇   For Windows Vista, the main panel shows the worksheets supplied with MINITAB; these will not be used in M248. Click on your user account icon to the left of the main panel. Then double-click on **Documents** in the main panel. The list of folders in **Documents** will appear in the main panel.

◇   In the main panel, double-click on the folder **M248 Data Files**.

> For earlier Windows operating systems, click on the **My Documents** icon to the left of the main panel.
>
> It will look different for Windows Vista and Windows XP.

The worksheets in the folder will be listed in the main panel. Figure 1.2 shows the **Open Worksheet** dialogue box for Windows 7.

◇   Scroll through the list of file names in the main panel until you find **tattoos.mtw**, then double-click on it. The message 'A copy of the content of this file will be added to the current project' will be displayed.

◇   Click on **OK** and the data will be displayed in the Data window.

> Alternatively, you can open a worksheet by clicking on its name to select it, then on **Open**; or you can type its name in the **File name** field, then click on **Open**.

MINITAB contains a description of the data in each of the M248 data files. View a description of the data in the worksheet **tattoos.mtw**, as follows.

◇   Click on **File**, then choose **Worksheet Description...** from the menu (by clicking on it). The **Worksheet Description** dialogue box will open.

Figure 1.2 The **Open Worksheet** dialogue box

The number of file names shown in the main panel may not be exactly the same on your computer.

A description of the data is contained in the **Comments** field of the dialogue box. When you have read the description, click on **OK** (or **Cancel**) to close the dialogue box.

The cells in a Data window contain values that you have retrieved by opening a worksheet or that you have typed in directly. The Data window is *not* a spreadsheet. Cells do not contain formulas: although you can create new columns of values using values in existing columns, the values in the new columns do *not* update automatically when values in the existing columns are changed.

Computer Activity 1.3   *Opening a second worksheet*

You can have several worksheets open at the same time. The worksheet **nuclear.mtw** contains data on the number of nuclear power stations in various countries prior to 1989. Open this worksheet now.

These data are described in Example 1.1 of *Unit A1*.

A second Data window opens; it is called **nuclear.mtw**. This window becomes the active window when the worksheet is opened.

◇   Click on **Window** to view the contents of the **Window** menu.

Notice that four windows are listed in the bottom section of the menu as four windows are currently open. These are the Session window, the Project Manager window and two Data windows, **nuclear.mtw** and **tattoos.mtw**. Also, notice that there are three asterisks next to the file name **nuclear.mtw**, but there are no asterisks next to **tattoos.mtw**. The three asterisks indicate that **nuclear.mtw** is the *current* worksheet. When a worksheet is opened, it becomes the current worksheet. When you produce graphs and perform statistical calculations, the operations are carried out using the data in the current worksheet. The **Comments** field of the **Worksheet Description** dialogue box will contain a description of the current worksheet.

If you want a different open worksheet to be the current one, make its Data window active; it then becomes the current worksheet. A Data window is made active either by clicking anywhere on the worksheet (if it is visible) or using the **Window** menu: simply click on the name of the worksheet in the menu and its Data window will become active. Before moving on to the next section, spend a few minutes checking that you can make a different Data window active (and hence change the current worksheet).

If you intend to proceed directly to the next section, then do not close the worksheets **tattoos.mtw** and **nuclear.mtw**. You will need these worksheets open for the activities in Section 1.2.

1.2 *Producing a pie chart*

In this section, you will learn how to produce a pie chart using MINITAB. You should have the worksheets **tattoos.mtw** and **nuclear.mtw** open. If not, then open them now, and make **tattoos.mtw** the current worksheet.

Computer Activity 1.4   *A pie chart for tattoo size*

In this activity, you will obtain a pie chart for tattoo size similar to the one in Figure 2.1 of *Unit A1*.

Pie charts are produced using **Pie Chart...** from the **Graph** menu.

◇   Click on **Graph**, then choose **Pie Chart...** from the menu (by clicking on it). The dialogue box shown in Figure 1.3 will open.

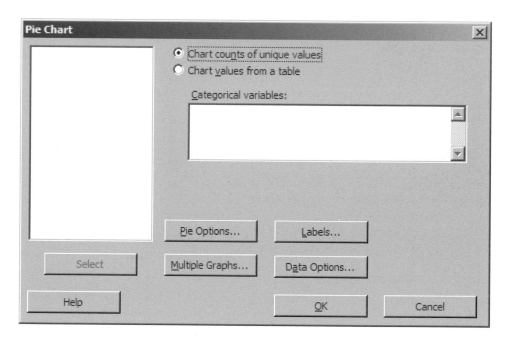

Figure 1.3   The **Pie Chart** dialogue box

First, you must specify the data to be used for the pie chart.

◇   Place the cursor in the **Categorical variables** field in the dialogue box (by clicking on the field). The numbers and names of the columns of the active worksheet (**tattoos.mtw**) will then be listed in the panel on the left-hand side of the dialogue box.

◇   A pie chart for the data on tattoo size is required, so type C3 (or `size`) in the **Categorical variables** field.

◇   Click on the **Labels...** button near the bottom of the **Pie Chart** dialogue box.

Alternatively, you could double-click on C3 `size` in the list on the left, or click on C3 `size` and then click on the **Select** button.

A **Pie Chart - Labels** dialogue box will open. This dialogue box consists of two panels. As its name suggests, the **Titles/Footnotes** panel is used for specifying the title of the pie chart and any subtitles or footnotes.

◇   Type `Size of tattoos` in the **Title** field.

The **Slice Labels** panel is used for choosing the labelling of the slices on the pie chart.

◇   Click on the **Slice Labels** tab to view this panel.

The default is for the individual slices to be unlabelled, although the pie chart will have a key (or legend). In Figure 2.1 of *Unit A1*, each slice is labelled with the category name and a line is drawn from the label to the slice. Produce a pie chart labelled in this way, as follows.

◇   Click on **Category name** (or on its check box) to select it.

◇   Click on **Draw a line from label to slice** (or on its check box) to select it.

Ticks will appear to indicate that these options have been selected.

◇   Click on **OK** to close the **Pie Chart - Labels** dialogue box.

◇   Now click on **OK** in the **Pie Chart** dialogue box, and a pie chart similar to the one in Figure 1.4 will be displayed in a Graph window.

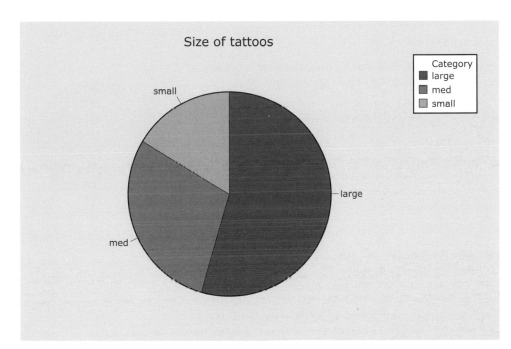

The pie chart on your computer screen will be coloured, not black and white and shades of grey.

Figure 1.4   A pie chart for tattoo size

Notice that MINITAB includes a key (or legend) with the pie chart. Since the individual slices have been labelled, this is not needed here. Remove the legend, as follows.

◇   Click on the legend to select it. The solid black squares around the edge of the legend indicate that it has been selected.

◇   Press the **Delete** key on your keyboard, and the legend will be deleted.

Comment

When producing a pie chart in MINITAB, by default the starting point for drawing the first slice is the 12 o'clock position and angles are measured clockwise from there. You can change the starting position by clicking on **Pie Options...** in the **Pie Chart** dialogue box to obtain the **Pie Chart - Options** dialogue box. Then type an angle (in degrees) in the field labelled **Start angle** in the **Pie Chart - Options** dialogue box. You can also specify the order in which the slices are drawn. For text categories, as here, the default is to place the slices in alphabetical order.

See MINITAB Help for more information on the options available.

Computer Activity 1.5   *Another pie chart for tattoo size* _____

One way of emphasizing the data on the number of small tattoos is by pulling out the slice for this category. You can do this by editing the pie chart you produced in Computer Activity 1.4, as follows.

◇   Click on the pie chart to select it. The solid black squares on the pie chart indicate that it has been selected. (All the slices will be selected.)

◇   Click on the slice labelled `small`, so that only this slice is selected.

◇   Double-click on this slice while it is selected. The **Edit Pie** dialogue box will open. (Alternatively, press **Ctrl+T** while the slice is selected to open this dialogue box; or right-click on this slice—that is, click on the slice using the right-hand mouse button—and choose **Edit Pie...** from the menu that appears.)

◇   Click on the **Explode** tab to view the **Explode** panel.

◇   Select **Explode slice** in the **Explode** panel.

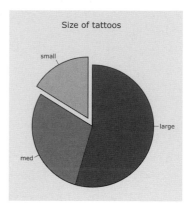

The value in the **Explode length** field determines how far out the slice is pulled. This value must be a number between 0 and 1. Leave the default value (0.5) in this field.

◇   Click on **OK**, and the slice will be pulled out as shown in Figure 1.5.

Note that the slice will still be selected on your graph. It will be deselected automatically when you select another part of the graph (by clicking on it). However, if you do not want any part of a graph to be selected, then right-click anywhere within the Graph window, move the mouse pointer to **Select Item** in the menu that is displayed, and click on **None**.

Figure 1.5   Another pie chart for tattoo size

Comment

When producing a pie chart, you cannot specify in advance that a slice is to be pulled out. This can be done only by editing the pie chart after it has been produced, as described above. More options are available for customizing a pie chart after it has been produced than before. In general, you can edit any part of a Graph window by selecting it and using the corresponding **Edit** dialogue box: this dialogue box can be obtained either by double-clicking on the selected item, or by pressing **Ctrl+T**, or by clicking on the selected item with the right-hand mouse button and choosing the **Edit** option from the menu that is displayed (**Edit Pie...**, **Edit Legend...**, and so on).

Computer Activity 1.6   *Quality of tattoo removal* _____

The numbers in the column labelled `score` in the Data window for **tattoos.mtw** reflect the quality of tattoo removal: 1 represents a poor removal and 4 represents an excellent result. Produce a pie chart with the title `Quality of tattoo removal`, with the slices labelled with both frequencies and percentages and with lines drawn from the labels to the slices.

You should now have produced three pie charts (one in Computer Activity 1.4, which you edited to produce a second in Computer Activity 1.5, and one in this activity). The pie charts you produced in Computer Activity 1.5 and in this activity are in separate Graph windows.

In general, if you do not want to keep a graph, then it is good practice to close its window. Otherwise, your screen can quickly become cluttered. You can close a Graph window at any time by making it active and then clicking on the cross in the top right-hand corner of the window. You will not be asked to use any of the graphs you have already produced, so close their windows now.

Comment

When you opened the **Pie Chart** dialogue box to produce the pie chart in this
activity, the settings were those you chose in Computer Activity 1.4: once you
have chosen settings and options in any dialogue box, they remain unchanged for
the duration of your current MINITAB session, or your current project. (Project
files are discussed in Section 1.3.) This feature of MINITAB is often useful.

When using MINITAB to create a pie chart, the data may be entered in the
worksheet either in *raw form* or in *summary form*. The data on tattoo removal
are in raw form: each row of the worksheet corresponds to a single observation.
The data in **nuclear.mtw** are in summary form: the first column contains the
category names (country) and the second contains frequencies for the categories
(number).

When producing a pie chart, you must specify the form in which the data are
stored. (The default is raw form.) Computer Activity 1.7 involves obtaining a pie
chart for the data on nuclear power stations which are stored in summary form.

Computer Activity 1.7   Nuclear power stations

Make the Data window for **nuclear.mtw** the active window. Then choose **Pie
Chart...** from the **Graph** menu to obtain the **Pie Chart** dialogue box.

> Click on **nuclear.mtw** in the **Window** menu to make the **nuclear.mtw** worksheet the active window.

When the data are in summary form, you need to select **Chart values from a
table** (instead of **Chart counts of unique values**, which is used when the data
are in raw form).

◇   Click on **Chart values from a table** or on its radio button to select it.
    Notice that the **Categorical variables** field is replaced by two fields,
    labelled **Categorical variable** and **Summary variables.**

◇   Place the cursor in the **Categorical variable** field (by clicking on the field).
    The data columns will be listed on the left of the dialogue box.

◇   The categories are in C1 country, so enter C1 (or country) in the
    Categorical variable field.

> Either type C1 or (country), or double-click on C1 country in the list on the left, or highlight C1 country and click on **Select**.

◇   Now place the cursor in the **Summary variables** field. Notice that
    MINITAB expects numeric data for frequencies, so it does not list columns
    containing non-numeric data.

◇   Enter C2 (or number) in the **Summary variables** field.

Obtain a pie chart with the title Nuclear power stations, with the slices
labelled with the category names and frequencies, and with lines connecting the
labels to the slices. With this labelling, a legend is not needed, so delete the
legend (by selecting it and pressing the **Delete** key).

Computer Activity 1.8   Combining categories

A journalist writing about the distribution of nuclear power stations argues that
it is not worth displaying separately information for countries with less than 5%
of the total number of stations. Obtain a pie chart similar to the one you
obtained in Computer Activity 1.7, but with countries with less than 5% of the
total number of nuclear power stations combined into one group.

> One of the options in the **Pie Chart - Options** dialogue box allows you to combine the smallest categories.

The pie charts in Figure 1.6 are the ones you obtained in Activities 1.7 and 1.8, but without the frequencies.

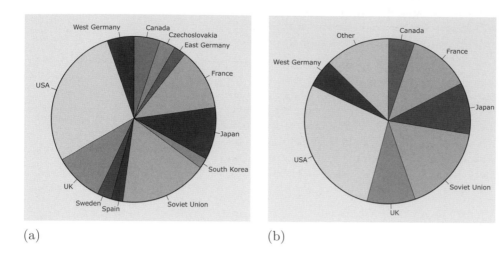

(a)   (b)

Figure 1.6   Pie charts showing numbers of nuclear power stations

It is not easy to extract meaningful information from a pie chart as detailed as the one in Figure 1.6(a) because of the large number of slices, some of which are quite small. For data with a large number of categories, it is common practice to produce a pie chart which displays the main categories and groups together the smaller ones. In Computer Activity 1.8, you did this by combining the categories for countries with less than 5% of the total number of power stations. This resulted in a pie chart similar to Figure 1.6(b). This figure also contains a lot of information and it is still not easy to extract meaningful information.

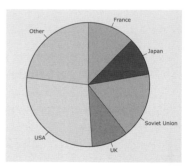

Figure 1.7   A pie chart with the smallest groups combined

Combining the categories for countries with less than 8% of the total number of nuclear power stations results in a pie chart similar to Figure 1.7.

Although this display is simpler than the previous ones, it is unsatisfactory for a different reason: too much information has been lost. For instance, you cannot now compare France's nuclear power provision with that of West Germany.

Pie charts are of limited use because they can give an immediate visual impression of proportion for only a small number of categories. Nevertheless, the pie chart is one of the most common methods used by the media to display information: you can find a pie chart in the business section of a daily newspaper on most days.

In this section you have used several of the options available for producing and editing pie charts. Before moving on to the next section, spend a few minutes exploring the effects of the remaining options.

You should now have two worksheets and at least one Graph window open. Do not close them: keep them open for use in Section 1.3. (You may have several Graph windows open if you produced further graphs when exploring the options available for pie charts.)

1.3 Saving your work

One of the most frustrating things about using software packages is that, if you have to quit a session before you have finished, many of them require you to start afresh the next time you run the package. This is not the case with MINITAB. You can save your session in a *project file* and then pick up from where you left off whenever you choose by opening the file.

When you begin a MINITAB session, a new project file is opened automatically, so you do not have to remember to open a project file at the beginning of a session.

Computer Activity 1.9   Saving your session in a project file ————

Use the following instructions to save your current session in a project file named **project1.mpj**, as follows.

◇   Choose **Save Project** from the **File** menu. The **Save Project As** dialogue box will open.

◇   If necessary, navigate to the **M248 Data Files** folder.

◇   Type project1 in the **File name** field.

◇   Click on **Save** or press **Enter**.

Project files have the file name extension **mpj**. MINITAB adds **.mpj** automatically.

At any time, you can view a session that you have saved as a project by opening the project file. Choose **Open Project...** from the **File** menu to obtain the **Open Project** dialogue box, navigate to the folder where the project file is located, and double-click on the file name. You will find that your project is restored exactly as you left it, complete with worksheets, graphs, etc. and you can carry on from where you left off. If, after further work, you wish to save your session under a different file name, choose **Save Project As...** from the **File** menu. You will be offered the chance to choose another file name. Choosing **Save Project** instead will, of course, overwrite the old file with the modified one.

Note that when you choose **Exit** from the **File** menu, you will be asked whether or not you wish to save either your whole project or parts of it.

The contents of an individual window may be saved by making the window active and then choosing the appropriate **Save... As** command from the **File** menu (for example, **Save Graph As...** or **Save Session Window As...** or **Save Current Worksheet As...**). The M248 data files are read-only, so you will have to use **Save Current Worksheet As...** rather than **Save Current Worksheet** if you wish to save a data file that you have changed.

If you accidentally delete a data file then you will need to reinstall the M248 data files in order to obtain a copy of the file.

If you wish to save a project or graph (or whatever) in a different folder from that containing the M248 MINITAB data files, then navigate to the directory you want to use, then click on **Save**.

By the way, you can edit the Session window. This means that you can remove unwanted text and annotate your output, if you wish, before saving it.

1.4   The Project Manager

The **Project Manager** is discussed briefly in this section. It contains folders
that allow you to navigate, view and manipulate parts of your current project. In
Section 1.3, you saved a session of your work in a project file named
project1.mpj. Open this project if it is not already open, so that it is your
current project.

◇   Choose **Project Manager** from the **Window** menu to view the Project
Manager window. This contains two panels, as shown in Figure 1.8.

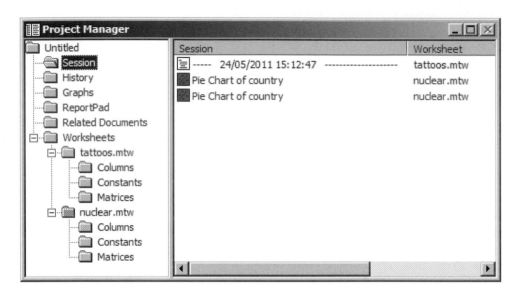

Figure 1.8   The Project Manager window

The left-hand panel shows the path structure of the project file. The contents of
the open folder are displayed in the right-hand panel. In Figure 1.8, the Session
folder is open; this contains a list of the graphs in the project file and the date
and time at which the project file was opened.

◇   Click on the History folder in the left-hand panel to open it and view its
contents in the right-hand panel. This folder contains a record of all the
commands carried out in the project.

◇   Click on the Graphs folder in the left-hand panel. The Graphs folder contains
a list of the graphs in the project.

◇   Click on the ReportPad folder. This folder contains the heading Minitab
Project Report. You can type text in the ReportPad window, copy text from
the Session window and insert MINITAB graphs. Some basic word-processing
facilities are available using ReportPad. (See MINITAB Help for further
details.)

◇   Click on the Related Documents folder. This contains a list of programs,
documents or internet URLs that are related to your MINITAB project (if
there are any). This folder is currently empty.

◇   Click on the Worksheets folder in the left-hand panel. The Worksheets folder
contains a subfolder for each worksheet that is open; in this project, two
worksheets are open — **nuclear.mtw** and **tattoos.mtw**.

◇   Click on the **nuclear.mtw** folder in the left-hand panel. Some information
about the data in the worksheet is displayed in the right-hand panel. (This
information can also be viewed using **Worksheet Description...** from the
File menu, as described in Computer Activity 1.2.)

Clicking on a worksheet folder or on its contents makes it the active worksheet.

◇   Click on the **tattoos.mtw** folder in the left-hand panel. The worksheet becomes the active worksheet, and information about the data is displayed in the right-hand panel.

◇   Now click on the **Columns** subfolder of the **tattoos.mtw** folder.

For each column containing data, the column name, the column number, the number of rows, the number of missing values, the column type and the column description (if any) are displayed. The letter T in the Type column for columns C1 to C4 indicates that these four columns contain some text characters. The letter N for column C5 indicates that this column contains numeric data only. A letter D means that a column contains dates or times — there is no column containing data of this type in the worksheet **tattoos.mtw**.

There are no constants or matrices in the worksheet, so the **Constants** and **Matrices** subfolders are empty. (See this for yourself by opening these subfolders.)

Spend a few minutes exploring the Project Manager window before continuing to the next section.

1.5   Printing output

Printing the contents of a MINITAB window is very simple.

◇   First make the window active.

◇   Then choose **Print Session Window...**, or **Print Worksheet...**, or **Print Graph...** from the **File** menu (as appropriate).

Although printing output in this way is very simple, it has the disadvantage that it can waste a whole sheet of paper on one comparatively small picture or on a small amount of text. If you are accustomed to word-processing, you may want to paste your output into a word-processor document and then print the document. Pasting output into a word-processor document is described in Section 1.6.

1.6   Pasting output into a word-processor document

Incorporating output from MINITAB into a word-processor document is straightforward. You need to have both your word processor and MINITAB running. The document in which you wish to insert MINITAB output should also be open.

The instructions in this section work for Microsoft Word and many other word processors.

Inserting graphical output

You can copy the graphical display in a Graph window and insert it into a word-processor document as follows.

◇   Make the Graph window active.

◇   Choose **Copy Graph** from the **Edit** menu (or press **Ctrl+C**, or click the *right* mouse button in the Graph window and choose **Copy Graph** from the menu that is displayed). This copies the graphical display to the Windows clipboard.

◇   Switch to your word processor. The easiest way to do this is to press **Alt+Tab**. (Alternatively, use the task bar to switch between applications.)

◇   Place the cursor at the point in your document where you wish to insert the graphical display.

◇   Finally, choose **Paste** from the **Edit** menu of your word processor (or press **Ctrl+V**) and the display will be inserted into your document.

Inserting text from MINITAB

You can copy text from any of the MINITAB windows and insert it into a word-processor document as follows.

◇   Highlight the text that you want to copy.

◇   Choose **Copy** from the **Edit** menu (or press **Ctrl+C**, or click the *right* mouse button in the window and choose **Copy** from the menu that is displayed). This copies the highlighted text to the Windows clipboard.

◇   Switch to your word processor.

◇   Place the cursor at the point in your document where you wish to insert the text.

◇   Choose **Paste** from the **Edit** menu (or press **Ctrl+V**) and the text will be inserted into your document.

Summary of Chapter 1

In this chapter, you have been introduced to the data analysis software package MINITAB. You have met many features of MINITAB in the context of producing pie charts for two of the data sets discussed in *Unit A1*.

You have seen that MINITAB stores data in files called worksheets; these have the file name extension **mtw**. A useful feature of MINITAB is the facility for saving sessions in files called projects; these have the file name extension **mpj**. If you save a completed session, then you can go over it again at a later stage and recall what you did. If you save an unfinished session as a project, then you can continue at a later time from where you left off.

You have also learned how to print output from MINITAB and how to paste output into a word-processor document.

Chapter 2
Bar charts

In this chapter, you will learn how to produce a bar chart using MINITAB. You will obtain bar charts similar to some of those described in *Unit A1*.

Bar charts are produced using **Bar Chart...** from the **Graph** menu. Several other kinds of chart can be produced using **Bar Chart...**, but the default is a bar chart. The other possibilities are not discussed in this chapter.

As was the case for pie charts, data may be either in raw form (one row of the worksheet for each observation) or in summary form (with values in one column of the worksheet and frequencies in a second column). As you saw in Chapter 1, the data on tattoo removal are stored in raw form and the data on the numbers of nuclear power stations in various countries are in summary form. In the activities in this chapter, you will see how to use **Bar Chart...** with data stored in either form. Some of the many options available with **Bar Chart...** are discussed briefly. When you have worked through the activities, you might like to explore some of the other options to see what they do.

Computer Activity 2.1   *Quality of tattoo removal* _____

In this activity you will obtain a bar chart similar to the one in Figure 2.4 of
Unit A1 for the data on the quality of tattoo removal. The data are in the
worksheet **tattoos.mtw**.

◇   Open this worksheet now.   **File > Open Worksheet...**

A reminder of how to do this is given in the margin. From now on, instead of
repeating detailed instructions, a reminder such as this one will often be given in
the margin. In this case the reminder indicates that you should choose **Open
Worksheet...** from the **File** menu.

Note that the data are in raw form, one row of the worksheet for each observation.

◇   Click on **Graph** and choose **Bar Chart...** (by clicking on it). The **Bar
     Charts** dialogue box shown in Figure 2.1 will open.

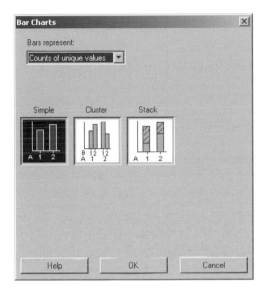

Figure 2.1   The **Bar Charts** dialogue box

At the top of the dialogue box, there is a field labelled **Bars represent**.

◇   Click on the arrow to the right of the field to view the **Bars represent**
     drop-down list.

This list contains three options. `Counts of unique values` (the default) is used
when the data are stored in raw form (as is the case here), and `Values from a
table` is used when the data are in summary form. The other option — `A
function of a variable` — will not be used in M248.

◇   The data are in raw form, so select `Counts of unique values`.

◇   Select a simple bar chart by clicking on the **Simple** diagram.   **Simple** is the default option.

◇   Click on **OK**, and the **Bar Chart - Counts of unique values, Simple**
     dialogue box will open.

To produce a bar chart for the quality of tattoo removal is straightforward. All
you need to do is enter the column containing the categories in the **Categorical
variables** field. Notice that any columns of the worksheet that contain data that
could be used for the categories are listed in the area on the left of the dialogue
box — all the columns are listed in this case. The categories correspond to the
quality of tattoo removal. This information is given in column C5 `score`.

◇   Enter C5 (or `score`) in the **Categorical variables** field.

◇   Click on **OK**, and the bar chart in Figure 2.2(a) will be produced.

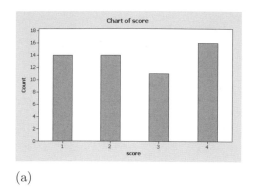 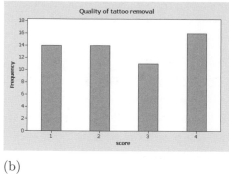

(a)   (b)

Figure 2.2   Two bar charts for quality of tattoo removal

Figure 2.2(b) is simply Figure 2.2(a) with the title and the *y*-axis label changed. To produce Figure 2.2(b), you need to edit the default title and label, as follows.

◇   Select the title (by clicking on it), then double-click on it (or press **Ctrl+T**) to open the **Edit Title** dialogue box.

◇   Replace the default title by typing the new title `Quality of tattoo removal` in the **Text** field near the bottom of the **Edit Title** dialogue box.

◇   Click on **OK**, and the title of the bar chart will be replaced.

◇   Now select the label on the vertical axis, then double-click on it (or press **Ctrl+T**) to open the **Edit Axis Label** dialogue box.

◇   Replace the default label by typing `Frequency` in the **Text** field of the **Edit Axis Label** dialogue box.

◇   Click on **OK** and the bar chart in Figure 2.2(b) will be produced.

Do not close the worksheet **tattoos.mtw**. You will need it for Computer Activity 2.2.

Computer Activity 2.2   *Displaying two data sets*

Now suppose that you wish to display the results on the quality of tattoo removal separately for deep tattoos and for tattoos of moderate depth, and so compare the success of the surgical procedure for tattoos of different depths. Figure 2.3 represents the same data on quality of tattoo removal as Figure 2.2(b), but with the results for deep tattoos and tattoos of moderate depth represented separately using bars drawn side-by-side on the same diagram.

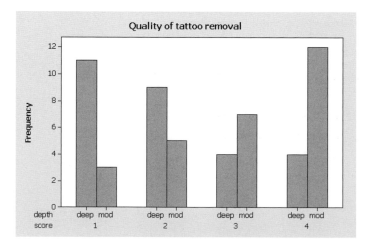

Figure 2.3   Quality of removal for tattoos of different depths

Since 1 represents a poor removal and 4 represents an excellent result, this diagram shows that the results of the surgical procedure were generally better for tattoos of moderate depth than for deep tattoos.

To obtain a bar chart like the one in Figure 2.3 with the results for different groups represented by adjacent bars on the same diagram you need to select the **Cluster** option in the **Bar Charts** dialogue box. Follow the instructions below to obtain this bar chart for yourself.

◇   Obtain the **Bar Charts** dialogue box.   **Graph > Bar Chart...**

◇   Select **Cluster** (by clicking on its diagram).

◇   Click on **OK** and the **Bar Chart - Counts of unique values, Cluster** dialogue box will open.

Next you must specify the variables to be used in the **Categorical variables** field.

You must specify the variable to be displayed first (`score`). You wish to display the results separately for tattoos of different depths, so next you must specify the variable which contains the depths (`depth`).

◇   Enter `score depth` in the **Categorical variables** field. (Enter the variables in that order — the order is important.)

◇   Click on **OK**, and a clustered bar chart will be displayed in a Graph window.

To reproduce Figure 2.3 exactly, you need to edit the title and the label on the vertical axis, as described in Computer Activity 2.1.

Select the title/label, then double-click on it (or press **Ctrl+T**) to open the **Edit Title/Edit Axis Label** dialogue box.

Now produce a similar bar chart to display separately the results on quality of tattoo removal for the two surgical methods.

Computer Activity 2.3 Nuclear power stations ─────────────

In this activity you will obtain a bar chart for the data on nuclear power stations similar to the one in Figure 2.3 of *Unit A1*. The data are in the worksheet **nuclear.mtw**. Open this worksheet now.

There are several points to note here. First, the data are stored in summary form in the worksheet. Secondly, the bars in Figure 2.3 of *Unit A1* are arranged in order of length so that the longest bar is first (at the top) and the shortest is last (at the bottom). Also, the bars in the figure are drawn horizontally instead of vertically. Finally, the labelling on the axes needs to be changed from the default to reproduce the figure from the unit.

◇   Obtain the **Bar Charts** dialogue box.   **Graph > Bar Chart...**

◇   The data are in summary form, so choose `Values from a table` from the **Bars represent** drop-down list.

◇   Select **Simple** (the default), and click on **OK**. The **Bar Chart - Values from a table, One column of values, Simple** dialogue box will open.

To display data in summary form, you must specify the column that contains the frequencies in the **Graph variables** field and the column containing the categories in the **Categorical variable** field.

◇   Enter `number` in the **Graph variables** field and `country` in the **Categorical variable** field.

The order of the bars is specified using the **Bar Chart - Options** dialogue box.

◇   Click on the **Chart Options...** button to open this dialogue box.

The default ordering displays the categories in numeric order when the categories are given in a numeric column or, for text columns, in the order that they first occur in the worksheet.

◇   Select **Decreasing Y** (by clicking on it or on its radio button).

With this option selected, the longest bar is drawn first and the shortest last.

◇   Click on **OK** to close the dialogue box.

To draw the bars horizontally instead of vertically, the scales on the axes must be transposed. This is done using the **Bar Chart - Scale** dialogue box.

◇ Click on the **Scale...** button to obtain the dialogue box.

◇ Select **Transpose value and category scales** (by clicking on it or on its check box), then click on **OK** to close the dialogue box.

◇ Click on **OK** in the main dialogue box to obtain a bar chart.

Finally delete the default title (select it then press the **Delete** key), delete the label country on the vertical axis, and change the label on the horizontal axis to Number of nuclear power stations. The bar chart will then be as shown in Figure 2.4.

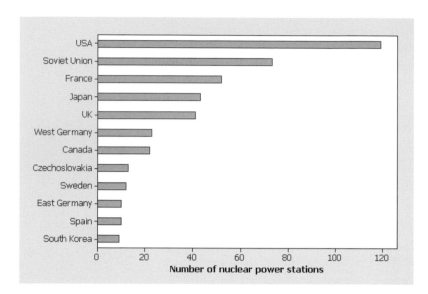

Figure 2.4 Nuclear power stations

Notice how much easier it is to compare the numbers of nuclear power stations in the countries using a bar chart like this one than it is using a pie chart such as that in Figure 1.6(a).

Computer Activity 2.4 The USA workforce

The data on the average composition of the USA workforce in 1986, which are given in Table 1.2 of *Unit A1*, are contained in the worksheet **usworkforce.mtw**. Produce a bar chart for the data with the bars drawn horizontally and with the data for males and females displayed separately. Label the lengths of the bars 'Millions' and order the bars so that the longest bar is at the top of the diagram.

There are many options available when using **Bar Chart...** from the **Graph** menu, and you have been introduced to only a small number of them. Now would be a good point at which to spend some time exploring some of the other options in order to find out what they do. How long you spend is entirely up to you. (You could use the worksheets used in this chapter for your exploration.)

Summary of Chapter 2

In this chapter you have learned how to produce a basic bar chart given data either in raw form or in summary form. You have seen how to change the axis labels, how to order the bars, how to draw the bars horizontally instead of vertically and how to display two data sets on the same diagram with the bars side-by-side. You have also been invited to explore some of the many options available for producing more sophisticated bar charts.

Chapter 3
Histograms and scatterplots

In this chapter you will learn how to produce histograms and scatterplots using MINITAB. Histograms are discussed in Section 3.1 and scatterplots in Section 3.2.

3.1 Histograms

Histograms are produced using **Histogram...** from the **Graph** menu. In this section you will obtain histograms similar to those in Figures 3.1 to 3.3 of *Unit A1* which represent the birth weights of 50 infants with severe idiopathic respiratory distress syndrome (SIRDS).

Computer Activity 3.1   Infants with SIRDS ────────────────

The birth weights of 50 infants with SIRDS are in the worksheet **sirds.mtw**. Open this worksheet now.

◇   Click on **Graph** and choose **Histogram...** (by clicking on it). The **Histograms** dialogue box will open.

◇   Select **Simple**, then click on **OK** to obtain the **Histogram - Simple** dialogue box.

◇   Enter `birthweight` in the **Graph variables** field at the top of the dialogue box.

The default options produce a histogram with the bars drawn vertically, the heights of the bars representing the frequencies in the intervals, with ticks on the horizontal axis at the midpoints of the intervals and with the intervals chosen by MINITAB.

◇   Click on **OK**, and a histogram will be produced.

Using the default options does not always produce a histogram with intervals that you would have chosen yourself. You can specify the intervals to be used by editing the bars on this histogram, as follows.

◇   Click on the bars to select them, then double-click on them (or press **Ctrl+T**).

◇   In the **Edit Bars** dialogue box, click on the **Binning** tab to view the **Binning** panel.

To produce a histogram similar to Figure 3.1 of *Unit A1*, you first need to say whether you would like ticks at the midpoints or at the cutpoints of the intervals.

◇   Under **Interval Type**, select **Cutpoint** to produce ticks at the borderlines between intervals.

Next you must specify the positions of the cutpoints.

◇   Under **Interval Definition**, select **Midpoint/Cutpoint positions**.

In the **Midpoint/Cutpoint positions** field, you must enter the positions of the cutpoints. You can do this by specifying the positions of the first and last cutpoints and the width of the intervals.

◇   Type `1:4/0.2` in the field.

Note the format of the entry: first cutpoint, colon, last cutpoint, forward slash, interval width.

◇   Click on **OK**, and the histogram in Figure 3.1 will be produced.

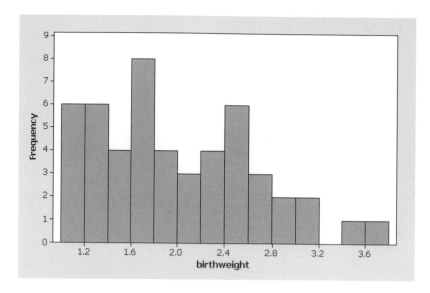

From now on in the computer books, the default title on a graphical display will often be omitted without comment when it is reproduced.

Figure 3.1   A histogram using 0.2 kg intervals

Many of the options available when using the **Histogram - Simple** dialogue box are similar to those available when using **Bar Chart....** You might like to explore some of the options later.

Computer Activity 3.2   *Using different intervals*

Obtain histograms for the SIRDS data similar to Figures 3.2, 3.3(a) and 3.3(b) of *Unit A1* (that is, with intervals of width 0.3 kg and with the first cutpoints at 1.0, 0.8 and 0.9, respectively).

Computer Activity 3.3   *Wages of production line workers*

The worksheet **uswages.mtw** contains data on the annual wages (in multiples of US$100) of a random sample of 30 production line workers in a large American industrial firm.

(a)   Obtain a histogram of the data using intervals of width 5.

(b)   Comment on the distribution of wages among the workers.

This would be a good point at which to spend a short time exploring the effects of the other options available when using **Histogram....**

3.2   Scatterplots

Scatterplots are produced using **Scatterplot...** from the **Graph** menu. In this section you will obtain scatterplots for the data on alcohol consumption and death rates from cirrhosis and alcoholism that are given in Table 1.5 of *Unit A1*, and for the data on the body weights and brain weights of animals given in Table 1.6 of *Unit A1*.

Computer Activity 3.4   *Alcohol-related deaths* _____

The worksheet **alcohol.mtw** contains the data given in Table 1.5 of *Unit A1* on alcohol consumption and death rates from cirrhosis and alcoholism. Open this worksheet now.

Follow the instructions below to obtain a scatterplot similar to Figure 3.4 of *Unit A1*.

◇   Choose **Scatterplot...** from the **Graph** menu.

◇   In the **Scatterplots** dialogue box, select **Simple** and click on **OK**.

The **Scatterplot - Simple** dialogue box is similar to those for producing simple bar charts and histograms. The main difference is in the area at the top: you must enter the names of the two variables to be plotted in row 1 under **Y variables** and **X variables**.

◇   Enter deathrate under **Y variables** and consumption under **X variables**.

◇   Click on **OK** to produce a scatterplot.

◇   Edit the axis labels so that the axes are labelled Consumption (litres per person) and Death rate (per 100000).

The scatterplot produced will be as shown in Figure 3.2.

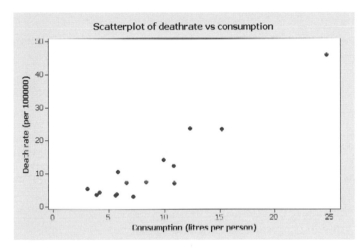

Figure 3.2   Alcohol-related deaths and alcohol consumption

Computer Activity 3.5   *Body weights and brain weights of animals* ___

The worksheet **weights.mtw** contains the data on the body weights and brain weights of animals given in Table 1.6 of *Unit A1*. Obtain a scatterplot of the data: enter brainweight under **Y variables** and bodyweight under **X variables** in the **Scatterplot - Simple** dialogue box. Label the axes Brain weight (g) and Body weight (kg).

Computer Activity 3.6   *Transforming the data using logarithms* _____

In *Unit A1* you saw that transforming the data using logarithms stretches out the lower values and compresses the larger ones. In this activity, two methods of producing a scatterplot with data transformed using natural logarithms are introduced.

The simpler method involves editing the scales of the scatterplot that you obtained in Computer Activity 3.5.

◇   Click on the scale on the horizontal axis to select it, then double-click on it (or press **Ctrl+T**).

◇   In the **Edit Scale** dialogue box, click on the **Transform** tab.

◇   In the **Transform** panel, select **Logarithm** under **Transformation**.

◇   Select e under **Base**.

◇   Click on **OK**. The scale on the horizontal axis will be transformed, and the tick labels will be powers of *e*.

◇　Now select the scale on the vertical axis, and transform it using logarithms using the same method to obtain the scatterplot in Figure 3.3(a).

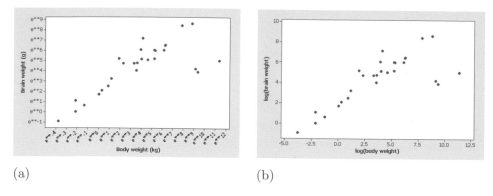

(a)   (b)

Figure 3.3　Body weights and brain weights after a log transformation

Alternatively, you can transform the data using **Calculator...** from the **Calc** menu and then obtain a scatterplot of the transformed data. Transform the data by taking natural logarithms, then store the results in columns named `log(body weight)` and `log(brain weight)`, as follows.

◇　Choose **Calculator...** from the **Calc** menu. The **Calculator** dialogue box will open.

◇　Initially, the cursor will be in the **Store result in variable** field. Type `log(body weight)` in the field.

◇　Now place the cursor in the **Expression** field.　　　　　　　　　Click in the field or press **Tab**.

◇　A list of functions available is given on the right of the dialogue box. Scroll through this list until you find `Natural log (log base e)`, select it (by clicking on it), then click on the **Select** button under the list of functions. `LN(number)` will be entered in the **Expression** field.

◇　The word `number` will be highlighted to indicate that you need to replace it with the name of the column where the data that you want to transform are stored. To do this, double-click on `C2 bodyweight` in the list of variables on the left of the dialogue box.

◇　Click on **OK** and the transformed data will be entered in the worksheet in a column (`C4` in this case) named `log(body weight)`.

◇　Now use a similar procedure to transform the data in `C3 brainweight` using logarithms and store the values in a column named `log(brain weight)`.

Use **Scatterplot...** from the **Graph** menu to obtain a scatterplot similar to Figure 3.3(b). (Enter `log(brain weight)` under **Y variables** and `log(body weight)` under **X variables** in row 1 in the **Scatterplot - Simple** dialogue box.)

Comment

Clearly, when producing a scatterplot for data transformed using logarithms, it is much quicker and easier to use the method of editing the scales than it is to use **Calculator....** However, when a different transformation is required, or when you wish to explore the transformed data other than by producing a scatterplot, you will have to use **Calculator...** to transform the data. Transformations are discussed further later in M248.

Summary of Chapter 3

In this chapter you have learned how to produce a histogram and how to choose the groups to be used. You have also learned how to produce a scatterplot for paired data, how to transform the data using natural logarithms and how to produce a scatterplot of the transformed data.

Chapter 4
Numerical summaries

Numerical summaries are produced using **Basic Statistics** from the **Stat** menu.
You can either display a fixed list of numerical summaries in the Session window,
or you can select the summaries you want from a list and either display the results
in the Session window or store the results in the worksheet. In the following
activities you will see how to do each of these. Several of the data sets discussed in
Unit A1 will be used to illustrate the use of MINITAB to find summary statistics.

Computer Activity 4.1   Family sizes of Ontario mothers ─────────

Data on the family sizes of Ontario mothers are contained in the worksheet
mothers1.mtw. Open this worksheet now. The data for the mothers with seven
years or more of education are in a column named **long**; the data for the mothers
with six years or less of education are in a column named **short**.

These data were introduced in
Example 4.8 of *Unit A1*.

Follow the instructions below for using **Basic Statistics** to find numerical
summaries for the mothers who had seven or more years of education.

◇　Move the mouse pointer to **Basic Statistics** in the **Stat** menu and choose
Display Descriptive Statistics... from the **Basic Statistics** submenu.

◇　Enter **long** in the **Variables** field of the **Display Descriptive Statistics**
dialogue box and click on **OK**.

The following output will be displayed in the Session window.

Variable	N	N*	Mean	SE Mean	StDev	Minimum	Q1	Median	Q3
long	35	0	4.800	0.668	3.954	0.000	2.000	4.000	6.000

Variable	Maximum
long	16.000

Several of the statistics displayed are self-explanatory. The mean and standard
deviation are 4.8 and 3.954, respectively. The maximum and minimum values
are 16 and 0, so the range is 16. **Q1** and **Q3** are the lower and upper quartiles, so
the interquartile range is $6 - 2 = 4$.

These are the results obtained
in Exercise 4.1 of *Unit A1*.

SE Mean is the *standard error of the mean*. This is a quantity that you will meet
later in M248: for the present you need only note that it is given, but not worry
about what it is. **N** is the number of values in the column and **N*** is the number of
missing values.

Use **Display Descriptive Statistics...** to obtain numerical summaries for the
family sizes of mothers with six years of education or less and compare your
results with those obtained in Exercise 4.1 of *Unit A1*.

You can specify which summary statistics are displayed by selecting from a list, as
follows.

◇　Obtain the **Display Descriptive Statistics** dialogue box.

**Stat > Basic Statistics >
Display Descriptive
Statistics...**

◇　Click on the **Statistics...** button to open the **Display Descriptive
Statistics - Statistics** dialogue box. This dialogue box contains a list of the
numerical summaries that can be displayed and a check box for each
summary.

◇　Deselect **SE of mean** and **N missing** (by clicking on them or on their check
boxes).

◇　Click on **OK** to close this dialogue box, then click on **OK** again.

Notice that **N*** and **SE mean** are not included in the output in the Session window.
They will not be included in output from **Display Descriptive Statistics...**
until you either change the statistics selected or start a new MINITAB project or
session.

Computer Activity 4.2 *Storing numerical summaries* _____

All of the numerical summaries that are available when **Display Descriptive Statistics...** is used can also be obtained using **Store Descriptive Statistics...** from the **Basic Statistics** submenu. In this activity, you will use **Store Descriptive Statistics...** to obtain the sample skewness for the family sizes of each of the two groups of Ontario mothers. If you do not have the worksheet **mothers1.mtw** open, then open it now.

◇　Move the mouse pointer to **Basic Statistics** in the **Stat** menu and choose **Store Descriptive Statistics...** from the **Basic Statistics** submenu.

◇　To obtain numerical summaries for the mothers who had seven years or more of education, enter `long` in the **Variables** field of the **Store Descriptive Statistics** dialogue box.

◇　Click on the **Statistics...** button.

The **Store Descriptive Statistics - Statistics** dialogue box contains a list of numerical summaries. This list is the same as the list of summaries that are available when using **Display Descriptive Statistics...**. Notice that the skewness is one of the summaries available.

The default settings result in the mean and sample size being stored in the first two available columns of the worksheet.

◇　Click on the check boxes for the mean and the sample size (**N nonmissing**) to deselect these options, and select **Skewness**.

◇　Click on **OK** to close this dialogue box, then click on **OK** again.

The sample skewness will be stored in column C3 (the first available column). The value given is 1.35942, which is 1.36 when rounded to two decimal places: this is the value given in Subsection 4.3 of *Unit A1*.

Use **Store Descriptive Statistics...** to find the sample skewness of the data on the family sizes of the Ontario mothers who had six years or less of education. Compare this with the value given in Subsection 4.3 of *Unit A1*.

Computer Activity 4.3 *Birth weights of infants with SIRDS* _____

When using **Display Descriptive Statistics...** you can obtain a graphical display of the data at the same time as numerical summaries.

(a)　The data on the birth weights of infants with SIRDS given in Table 1.3 of *Unit A1* are in the worksheet **sirds1.mtw**. Open this worksheet now.

Follow the instructions below for obtaining a histogram for the birth weights of the infants who survived, together with numerical summaries of the data.

◇　Obtain the **Display Descriptive Statistics** dialogue box.

◇　Enter `survived` in the **Variables** field.

◇　Now click on the **Graphs...** button to see what displays are available.

◇　Select **Histogram of data** from the list and click on **OK**.

◇　Click on **OK** in the **Display Descriptive Statistics** dialogue box.

Stat > Basic Statistics > Display Descriptive Statistics...

The numerical summaries will be displayed in the Session window and a histogram will be displayed in a Graph window.

Using the histogram, comment on whether you think the data are symmetrical, left-skew or right-skew.

Use **Store Descriptive Statistics...** to find the sample skewness of the birth weights. Does the value given confirm the answer you gave concerning the skewness of the data using only the histogram?

(b)　Repeat part (a) for the birth weights of the infants who died.

(c)　Use the output in the Session window to compare the means and standard deviations of the birth weights of the infants who survived and the infants who died.

Computer Activity 4.4   *More on obtaining numerical summaries* _____

The data on the birth weights of the infants with SIRDS are also given in the worksheet **sirds.mtw**. However, in this worksheet they are arranged differently. Open this worksheet now.

The birth weights of all the infants are given in column C1. Column C2 contains a categorical variable `survival` that indicates whether or not each infant died. (This variable is a 'text' variable — that is, one that contains text rather than numbers. This is obvious from the values of the variable, but it is also indicated by the fact that the column is headed C2-T. If it were a numeric variable, the label at the top would simply say C2.)

The numerical summaries and histograms that you found in the previous activity using **Display Descriptive Statistics. . .** may be found in a similar way using this worksheet.

◇   Obtain the **Display Descriptive Statistics** dialogue box.

◇   Enter `birthweight` in the **Variables** field.

◇   To obtain the numerical summaries for the infants who survived and the infants who died separately, enter `survival` in the **By variable** field.

If you are continuing directly from Computer Activity 4.3, then the numerical summaries and graphs selected will be those used in that activity, so you do not need to select them again.

◇   Click on **OK**.

Check that the results displayed are the same as those that you obtained in the previous activity.

Notice that the histograms are displayed in separate panels of a single Graph window.

Now use **Store Descriptive Statistics. . .** to obtain the sample skewness of the birth weights of the two groups of infants. Again you must select **By variable** and enter `survival` in its field. Notice how the results are stored in the worksheet.

Summary of Chapter 4

In this chapter, you have learned how to obtain numerical summaries of data using **Display Descriptive Statistics. . .** and **Store Descriptive Statistics. . .** from the **Basic Statistics** submenu of the **Stat** menu. You have also seen how to obtain a graphical display of the data when using **Display Descriptive Statistics. . . .**

Chapter 5
Boxplots

Boxplots are produced in MINITAB using **Boxplot. . .** from the **Graph** menu. In Section 5.1, you will learn how to obtain a 'simple' boxplot for a single data set. In Section 5.2, you will obtain comparative boxplots similar to those you have seen in *Unit A2*. In Section 5.3, you will learn how to use MINITAB to transform data to reduce skewness and hence produce more helpful boxplots.

5.1 Simple boxplots

In Example 1.1 of *Unit A2*, the construction of a simple boxplot was illustrated using data on the β endorphin concentrations of collapsed runners after the Great North Run. These data will be used in Computer Activities 5.1 and 5.2 to describe the use of MINITAB to produce a simple boxplot.

Computer Activity 5.1 *Collapsed runners: producing a 'default' boxplot*

The data on β endorphin concentrations in collapsed runners after the Great North Run are in the MINITAB worksheet **runners.mtw**. Open this worksheet now. The worksheet also includes the data from Table 1.4 of *Unit A1*, for runners who did not collapse. The data for the collapsed runners are in the third column, named `collapsed`. In this activity you will obtain MINITAB's default version of a boxplot for these data.

◇ Click on **Graph** and choose **Boxplot....**

The **Boxplots** dialogue box will open. It is very similar to those for **Histograms** and **Scatterplots** that you used in Chapter 3.

◇ To produce a simple boxplot for a single variable, under **One Y**, select **Simple** (the default option) and click on **OK**.

The **Boxplot - One Y, Simple** dialogue box will open. Essentially the fields and buttons in this dialogue box work in much the same way as they do when producing a simple histogram or scatterplot. Further options for customizing a boxplot are available once it has been produced. As for bar charts, histograms and scatterplots, changing an item in a graph is done by selecting it, then double-clicking on it (or pressing **Ctrl+T**) to open an **Edit** dialogue box. You will use some of these editing facilities in this chapter. You may like to try out some of the other options later.

Obtain a default boxplot for the data for the collapsed runners, as follows.

◇ Enter `collapsed` in the **Graph variables** field at the top of the dialogue box.

◇ Click on **OK** and the boxplot in Figure 5.1 will be produced.

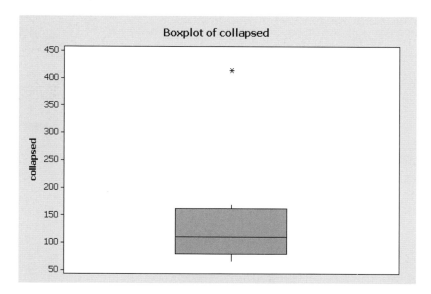

Figure 5.1 Default MINITAB boxplot for data on collapsed runners

Compare this boxplot with the boxplot for this data set in Figure 1.1 of *Unit A2*.

Comment

The main difference between the boxplot in Figure 5.1 and the boxplot in *Unit A2* is that MINITAB has drawn the boxplot vertically rather than horizontally. Apart from that, the positions of the 'box', the 'whiskers' and the potential outlier are shown in the same way as in Figure 1.1 of *Unit A2*. The vertically drawn boxplot is produced by MINITAB as a default: in other words, the program always draws boxplots vertically unless you ask it to draw them horizontally. There is no hard and fast rule about whether boxplots should be drawn vertically or horizontally. It is merely a question of personal preference.

You will see how to produce a horizontal boxplot in the next activity.

Computer Activity 5.2   *Collapsed runners: producing a horizontal boxplot*

To obtain a horizontal boxplot, you need to change one of the settings from the default.

◇   Obtain the **Boxplots** dialogue box.   **Graph > Boxplot...**

◇   Select **Simple** under **One Y** and click on **OK**.

◇   In the **Boxplot - One Y, Simple** dialogue box, click on **Scale...** to open the **Boxplot - Scale** dialogue box.

◇   To draw a horizontal boxplot, the option **Transpose value and category scales** in the **Axes and Ticks** panel of the **Boxplot - Scale** dialogue box must be selected. Select it now by clicking on it (or on its check box).

◇   Click on **OK** to close the dialogue box, then click on **OK** in the **Boxplot - One Y, Simple** dialogue box to produce the boxplot.

Alternatively, you can produce a horizontal boxplot by editing the vertical boxplot that you obtained in Computer Activity 5.1, as follows.

◇   Select the scale on the boxplot, then double-click on it (or press **Ctrl+T**) to open the **Edit Scale** dialogue box.

◇   In the **Scale** panel of the **Edit Scale** dialogue box, select **Transpose value and category scales**.

◇   Click on **OK** and a horizontal boxplot will be produced.

Which boxplot do you prefer — the vertical boxplot of Figure 5.1 or the horizontal boxplot produced in this activity?

Computer Activity 5.3   *Boxplot of silica data* ————————

In Activity 1.1 of *Unit A2*, you drew (by hand!) a boxplot for the data on silica content of meteorites. The data are in the MINITAB worksheet **silica.mtw**.

You met these data first in Activity 4.5 of *Unit A1*.

Obtain a horizontal boxplot for the data. Check that it matches the boxplot you drew in Activity 1.1 of *Unit A2*.

If you have not kept the boxplot you drew, then see Figure 1.5 of *Unit A2*.

The title and the axis label can be edited using the same method as for other graphs. Change the axis label to `Percentage silica`.

Select the axis label, and double-click on it (or press **Ctrl+T**).

5.2   Comparative boxplots

Producing comparative boxplots in MINITAB is also straightforward. The option selected in the **Boxplots** dialogue box depends on how the data are arranged in the worksheet.

Computer Activity 5.4   *Boxplots of SIRDS data* ————————

The data on the birth weights of infants with SIRDS, which were used to produce Figure 1.6 of *Unit A2*, are stored in the worksheet **sirds.mtw**. Open this worksheet now.

Each row of the worksheet contains the data for one infant. There are two columns. The first column contains the birth weights (in kg) of the infants in a variable called `birthweight`. The second column tells you whether or not each infant survived. This variable is called `survival`.

◇   Obtain the **Boxplots** dialogue box.   **Graph > Boxplot...**

◇   The data are in a single column, with groups given in a second column, so to obtain comparative boxplots, select **With Groups** under **One Y**. The **Boxplot - One Y, With Groups** dialogue box will open.

◇   Enter `birthweight` in the **Graph variables** field and `survival` in the **Categorical variables for grouping** field.

MINITAB is now set up to produce comparative boxplots. It will produce a boxplot of the data in the column `birthweight` for each distinct value in the column `survival`. Here there are two different values, `survived` and `died`, in the column `survival`, so two boxplots will be produced on a single diagram.

Produce both horizontal and vertical boxplots for the data.

Check that the horizontal boxplots look similar to those in Figure 1.6 of *Unit A2*. Do you prefer horizontal or vertical boxplots in this case?

Comment

In this case, the choice between horizontal and vertical boxplots is less clear-cut than it was for a simple boxplot. You may have preferred horizontal boxplots to vertical boxplots or vice versa. However, in the rest of this chapter (and the rest of M248), horizontal boxplots will be used consistently. You should keep in mind, though, that this decision is fairly arbitrary!

Computer Activity 5.5   *Boxplots of family sizes* ──────────

For the SIRDS data in Computer Activity 5.4, all the numeric data to be represented by boxplots were in one column. A variable in a second column indicated the different groups that were to be plotted separately. When the data are in this format, the **With Groups** option under **One Y** must be selected in the **Boxplots** dialogue box.

The family size data from Table 4.4 of *Unit A1* are in the worksheet **mothers1.mtw**. Open this worksheet now.

You will be using these data to produce boxplots like those in Figure 1.7 of *Unit A2*.

In this worksheet the two batches of data are in separate columns called `short` and `long` (indicating the different amounts of education that the mothers had had). To obtain comparative boxplots for data arranged like this, a different option in the **Boxplots** dialogue box is used.

◇   Obtain the **Boxplots** dialogue box.

Graph > Boxplot...

◇   Under **Multiple Y's**, select **Simple**, then click on **OK** to open the **Boxplot - Multiple Y's, Simple** dialogue box.

The name of each column for which a boxplot is required must be entered in the **Graph variables** field. The boxplot for the variable entered first will appear at the top of horizontal comparative boxplots, or on the left of vertical comparative boxplots. Obtain horizontal comparative boxplots with the boxplot for the mothers who had seven years or more of education at the top, as follows.

◇   Enter `long short` in the **Graph variables** field.

◇   Click on **Scale. . .**, and select **Transpose value and category scales** in the **Axes and Ticks** panel of the **Boxplot - Scale** dialogue box.

◇   Click on **OK** to close this dialogue box, then click on **OK** again to produce the comparative boxplots.

Next, give the two boxplots more meaningful labels on the vertical axis, as follows.

◇   Click on the vertical axis to select the vertical scale, and press **Ctrl+T** (or double-click on it while it is selected).

◇   Click on the **Labels** tab in the **Edit Scale** dialogue box to bring the **Labels** panel uppermost.

◇   Under **Major Tick Labels**, select **Specified** and type `more-education less-education` in its field.

◇   Click on **OK** and the labels will change.

Finally, delete the title and change the label on the common axis to `Number of children`.

Check that the resulting plot looks similar to Figure 1.7 of *Unit A2*.

Computer Activity 5.6   *Boxplots for diabetic mice* _____

The worksheet **diabetes.mtw** contains some data on bovine serum albumen (BSA) binding in normal mice treated with a placebo, alloxan-diabetic mice treated with a placebo and alloxan-diabetic mice treated with insulin. These data were discussed in Example 1.3 of *Unit A2*.

Produce horizontal comparative boxplots to compare the BSA binding levels in the three groups of mice, with the boxplot for alloxan-diabetic mice treated with insulin at the top, and the boxplot for normal mice treated with a placebo at the bottom. Delete the title, change the label on the common axis to BSA binding, and edit the labels for the individual boxplots so that the new labels are AD+insulin, AD+placebo and placebo.

5.3   Boxplots of transformed data

In some cases where patterns in the original data are obscured by skewness, more helpful comparative boxplots can be produced if the data are first transformed. This is true for the data on diabetic mice, for which you obtained boxplots in Computer Activity 5.6. In Computer Activity 5.7, you are asked to transform the data using logarithms and then produce boxplots of the transformed data.

Computer Activity 5.7   *Transforming the data* _____

For this activity, you will need the BSA binding data from the worksheet **diabetes.mtw**. In Example 1.3 of *Unit A2*, these data were transformed by taking logarithms. You learned how to use **Calculator...** in the **Calc** menu to transform data by taking logarithms in Chapter 3. With the data for the three groups of mice stored in separate columns, each column must be transformed separately. However, some time can be saved by stacking the three columns of data in one column and then transforming the data in this column. This is the approach that will be used here.

Data from several columns can be stacked in a single column using **Stack** from the **Data** menu. Stack the data in a single column named BSA and create a column named treatment identifying the groups of mice, as follows.

◇   Click on **Data**, move the mouse pointer to **Stack** and choose **Columns...** from the **Stack** submenu. The **Stack Columns** dialogue box will open.

◇   In the **Stack the following columns** field, enter the columns to be stacked — in this case, ADinsulin ADplacebo placebo.

◇   Under **Store stacked data in**, select **Column of current worksheet** and type BSA in its field.

◇   In the **Store subscripts in** field, type treatment, the name of the column where a record of the treatment received by each rat is to be stored.

◇   Click on **OK**.

The values from the columns will be listed in the column of stacked data in the order in which the column names are entered.

Two columns named BSA and treatment will be added to the worksheet.

Create a column called log(BSA) containing the natural logarithms of the BSA binding values.

Produce comparative boxplots of the transformed data.

Computer Activity 5.8   *The lifespan of rats* ————————————

The effect of a restricted diet versus an *ad libitum* diet (that is, free eating) on the total lifespan of rats was studied. Research indicates that diet restriction promotes longevity. Treatments were begun after an initial weaning period. The data are in the MINITAB worksheet **rats.mtw**. The lifespans (in days) of the rats with restricted diet are in the column **restricted**. The lifespans of the rats with unrestricted diet are in the column **unrestricted**.

Stack the data in a column named **lifespan**, and store the type of diet that each rat received in a column named **diet**. Obtain comparative boxplots for the lifespans of the two groups of rats. Comment briefly on the lifespans of the two groups of rats.

Berger, R.L., Boos, D.D. and Guess, F.M. (1988) Tests and confidence sets for comparing two mean residual life functions. *Biometrics*, **44**, 103–115.

You will have seen that there is some evidence of left skewness (long left tail) in the data on the lifespans of rats. The question arises of whether a clearer picture could be produced by transforming the data before producing boxplots. However, the logarithmic transformations that you have used so far will tend to 'squeeze up' the right tail of the data, thus making the boxplots even more left-skew. So logarithmic transformations will not help here.

Left-skew data can often be made more symmetric by squaring them (or more generally by raising them to a power greater than one). In Computer Activity 5.9, you will explore whether a square transformation helps here.

Computer Activity 5.9   *A square transformation* ————————————

A square transformation can be carried out in MINITAB using **Calculator...** from the **Calc** menu, as follows.

◇   Choose **Calculator...** from the **Calc** menu.

◇   Type the name of the column where the squared values are to be stored in the **Store result in variable** field; call it **squarelife** (say).

◇   Enter the expression **lifespan**2** in the **Expression** field.

◇   Click on **OK**.

Other powers can be dealt with in a similar way; basically ** means 'to the power of'.

Obtain comparative boxplots for the transformed data. Does the transformation make the comparison any clearer?

Computer Activity 5.10   *Effectiveness of insecticides* ————————————

For each of six different insecticides (labelled A, B, C, D, E and F), twelve batches of 50 insects were exposed to the insecticide for a fixed length of time. The resulting data are in the worksheet **insects.mtw**.

Lunneborg, C.E. (1994) *Modeling Experimental and Observational Data*. Duxbury Press, Ca., p. 150.

The numbers in the columns A, B, ..., F of the worksheet are the numbers of insects in the batches that are still alive (out of the 50) after the exposure time.

(a) Construct comparative boxplots for the numbers of insects left alive for each of the six insecticides. Label the common axis **Number of survivors**. Comment briefly on the numbers of survivors in the different batches.

(b) Do you think it would help to transform the data? Give reasons for your answer, and if you think the data should be transformed, suggest an appropriate transformation, make it, and produce boxplots of the transformed data.

Summary of Chapter 5

In this chapter you have learned how to produce boxplots, both simple and comparative, using MINITAB. You have also learned how to stack data from several columns into a single column, while producing another column that indicates where each data value came from. You have used **Calculator...** from the **Calc** menu to transform data by taking logarithms and by squaring them.

Chapter 6
Entering your own data

In this chapter, you will learn how to enter data from the computer keyboard in a MINITAB worksheet. The process is straightforward; put simply, all you have to do is to open a new blank worksheet and type in the data! Usually, in M248, the data that you will need to use in MINITAB will be stored in a worksheet, which you will have installed on your hard disk. However, in a few cases you will be asked to key in small data sets. Also, you may wish to use MINITAB to analyse your own data sets, and you may wish to enter small data sets so that you can draw graphs from them. To do these things, you need to know how to enter data in a worksheet.

A small data set from Example 2.2 of *Unit A2* will be used to illustrate how to enter data in a worksheet.

A study was carried out to investigate various aspects of early retirement from the British National Health Service (NHS). In 1998–99, 5469 NHS employees from England and Wales were granted early retirement because of ill health. The researchers examined the records for 1994 of these people. Table 6.1 (which is the same as Table 2.8 of *Unit A2*) gives data on these people, classifying each of them by occupational group and by a broad classification of the health reason for which they retired.

In this chapter you will be doing very little more than entering the data into a new MINITAB worksheet, so it does not matter if you have not yet read the corresponding section of *Unit A2*.

Pattani, S., Constantinovici, N. and Williams, S. (2001) Who retires early from the NHS because of ill health and what does it cost? A national cross sectional study. *British Medical Journal*, **322**, 208–209.

Table 6.1   Retirements from the NHS because of ill health, 1998–99

Occupational group	Reason for retiring because of ill health				
	Musculoskeletal	Psychiatric	Cardiovascular	Other	Total
Ambulance workers	65	12	6	12	95
Healthcare assistants or support	339	61	77	117	594
Nurses or midwives	364	144	70	153	731
Technical or professional staff	42	25	4	23	94
Administration or estates staff	118	94	31	66	309
Doctors or surgeons	33	40	20	28	121
Other	22	13	7	8	50
Total	983	389	215	407	1994

Computer Activity 6.1   *Entering the data in a worksheet* _____

Suppose that you want to enter these data in a MINITAB worksheet, perhaps so that you can produce some useful graphs. For instance, you might want to produce some bar charts showing how the people who retired for musculoskeletal, psychiatric, cardiovascular and other health reasons were divided between the different staff categories. How would you do it?

Actually, before you start, it is worth thinking about what you want to do with the data after they have been entered, as this may affect the way in which you enter the data. In this case, suppose that you want to produce a bar chart based on the values in the 'Musculoskeletal' column of Table 6.1, with a bar for each of the seven occupational groups. MINITAB expects the data for such a chart to appear in one of its columns, so the numbers in the 'Musculoskeletal' column of Table 6.1 would have to go into a column of a MINITAB worksheet.

However, if you wanted to use the data to produce some other sort of graph, another method of entering the data might be more appropriate. For instance, suppose you wanted to produce a pie chart from the data in the 'Doctors or surgeons' *row* of Table 6.1, with a 'slice' for each of the four categories of reasons for retirement. In this case, MINITAB would expect the data that it needs to calculate the size of each 'slice' to be in a column, not a row, and it would be best to change the way the data are arranged as you enter them in the worksheet, so that the rows in Table 6.1 correspond to columns in the MINITAB worksheet, and vice versa.

However, for this exercise, suppose that you want the columns in Table 6.1 to correspond to columns in the MINITAB worksheet, so that you can produce bar charts corresponding to the data in each column of Table 6.1.

The next question to consider, before you start typing in the data, is exactly which parts of Table 6.1 you need to enter. Often it is not necessary to enter absolutely every feature of a table in MINITAB. In this case, there seems little point in entering the row and column totals from Table 6.1. MINITAB can calculate these for you, if you need to use them.

> This can be done using **Row Statistics...** or **Column Statistics...** from the **Calc** menu.

So you will only need to enter the data from the first five columns (that is, the occupational group names together with the first four numerical columns) of Table 6.1 in a MINITAB worksheet. You can use the corresponding column headings from Table 6.1, or some abbreviated version of them, as names for the MINITAB columns. There is no need to enter the final (Total) row of Table 6.1 in MINITAB.

To enter the data, you need somewhere to enter it!

◇   In MINITAB, choose **New...** from the **File** menu.

A dialogue box will open. This allows you to choose whether you want a whole new project or simply a new worksheet within your current project.

◇   Click on **Minitab Project** to select it, and then click on **OK**.

If you are not beginning a new MINITAB session, you will be asked whether you want to save your current project. Then MINITAB will open a new project, with a new blank worksheet in it.

> If you wanted to work with your new worksheet as part of an existing project, you would choose **Minitab Worksheet** in the **New** dialogue box.

Make the worksheet window the active window. Your new worksheet window should look like the one in Figure 6.1. The active cell should initially be the cell below the column heading in the first column (`C1`), ready for you to enter a name for the column.

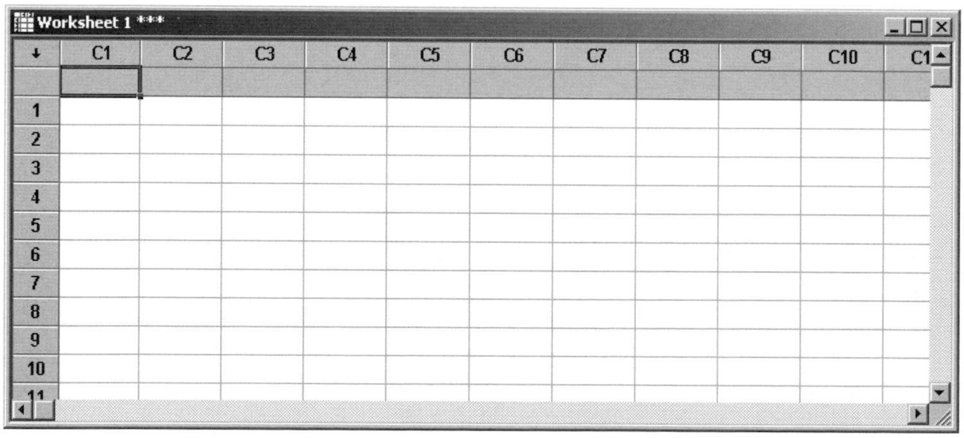

Figure 6.1   A new Worksheet window

There is a small arrow at the top left-hand corner of the Worksheet window. Initially, it should be pointing downwards (by default), but if it is pointing to the right, click on it (once) and it will point downwards. The significance of this arrow is explained later.

You could start entering the data straight away. However, it can be useful to name the columns you are going to use first. If you give the columns meaningful names at the outset, it can help you to enter the data values in the right positions, and to carry out your analyses on the correct data.

> You could defer naming the columns. Or you could simply not name them at all, and refer to them as `C1`, `C2`, and so on in your analyses.

If necessary, click in the cell below the column heading `C1` and above the first data cell in that column to make this cell the active cell. You can now type in some appropriate name for this column (which will include the names of the occupational groups from the first column of Table 6.1). MINITAB will allow you to use and save quite long column names (up to 31 characters), so you could use the whole column heading 'Occupational group', as in Table 6.1. However, snags can arise if you use long column names. For instance, only about the first 12 characters of column names appear in the fields in certain dialogue boxes, from which you can select variables for your analysis. Thus it is often advisable to keep column names fairly short. (This will save you some typing as well!) Therefore, call the first column simply 'group'.

◇   Type `group` in the space below `C1`.

◇   Now click in the space for the name of the second column, below `C2`. It will become the active cell.

This column is where you will enter the data from the 'Musculoskeletal' column of Table 6.1.

◇   Type `musculoskeletal` in this space, then click in the space for the name of the third column.

As already explained, since `musculoskeletal` contains more than 12 characters, a shorter title might have been advisable. However, notice that MINITAB expanded the column width automatically (after you made the space for the name of the next column the active cell) to make room for the name.

◇   Name the remaining three columns (`C3` to `C5`) `psychiatric`, `cardiovascular` and `other`, in a similar way.

If you find you have made a mistake in typing a name, then you can edit the name. Clicking once on a name selects it and allows you to type it all again. Double-clicking on a name puts a text editing cursor into the name, so that you can edit what you wrote rather than having to type it all again.

◇   Finally, click in the cell in row 1 of column 1, so that you are ready to enter the main data.

The first column will contain the occupational group titles. You could enter the full titles from Table 6.1 in the MINITAB worksheet—MINITAB will accept text values up to 80 characters long. However, as with long column names, this may not always be advisable. The longer the names are, the more problems arise from overlapping and illegible names on graphs, and on some graphs the full names may not appear. So it would be sensible to use shorter names. Thus the first group, ambulance workers, could be called simply 'ambulance'.

◇   Type `ambulance` in row 1 of column 1, and press **Enter**.

Apart from the word `ambulance` appearing where you typed it, two things have happened. First, the active cell is now the next cell down. That probably does not surprise you at all. It means that, if you have a long column of data to enter, you can just press **Enter** after each value and immediately start typing in the next cell. However, for some data sets, it might be more convenient to type all the values in a row, then move on to the next row, and so on. In this case, pressing **Enter** will make the wrong cell active. This is where the small arrow above the row numbers comes in. It is known as the 'entry direction' arrow. If you change the direction of the arrow by clicking on it (so that it points to the right rather than downwards), then pressing **Enter** will make the next cell to the right the active cell rather than the next cell down.

There are several other ways of moving from one cell of the worksheet to another. For instance, pressing **Tab** makes the next cell to the right the active cell; using the arrow keys on the keyboard moves the position of the active cell in the corresponding direction; and you can make any cell the active cell by clicking in the cell.

The other change that occurred when you pressed **Enter** after typing `ambulance` is that the label at the top of the column changed from `C1` to `C1-T`. MINITAB distinguishes between columns that contain text and columns that contain numeric data. It has recognized that you want the first column to contain text from the fact that you typed text in its first row, and has changed the column from numeric (the default) to text. If you had typed a number (or the symbol * that MINITAB uses to denote missing data values) instead of `ambulance`, this change would not have been made. MINITAB would treat the column as numeric, and would not allow you to type text into any of its cells. (You might wonder how you could enter a column of text, where the first entry happened to be a number. MINITAB allows you to change the type of a column from numeric to text, or vice versa, using **Change Data Type** from the **Data** menu.)

Columns used for storing dates or times are treated differently from those containing numeric or text data, but they will not be used in M248.

◇ Complete the data entry for the first column by typing suitably abbreviated versions of the names of the six remaining occupational groups in rows 2 to 7. If you make a mistake, you can edit the entries in the same way that you edit column names.

◇ Now click in the cell in row 1 of the second column, named `musculoskeletal`, and enter the appropriate number (65) from Table 6.1.

◇ Enter the other numbers in this column.

◇ Then go on to the other columns and enter the remaining numbers.

The completed worksheet should look like Figure 6.2 (except that you might have chosen different abbreviations in the first column).

	C1-T	C2	C3	C4	C5	C6	C7	C8	C9	C10
	group	musculoskeletal	psychiatric	cardiovascular	other					
1	ambulance	65	12	6	12					
2	healthassist	339	61	77	117					
3	nurses/midwives	364	144	70	153					
4	tech/prof	42	25	4	23					
5	admin/estates	118	94	31	66					
6	doctors/surgeons	33	40	20	28					
7	other	22	13	7	8					
8										
9										
10										
11										

Figure 6.2   The completed worksheet on NHS retirements

◇ Now that the worksheet is complete, save it, either on its own by using **Save Current Worksheet** or **Save Current Worksheet As...** from the **File** menu, or as part of a complete project using **Save Project** or **Save Project As...** from the **File** menu. Your new worksheet will work in the same way as those provided with the M248 materials.

For instance, you could save the worksheet in Figure 6.2 as **nhs.mtw.**

◇ Finally, display the data from the `musculoskeletal` column in a bar chart, showing how the retirements for musculoskeletal reasons are divided between the seven occupational groups.

Bar charts were discussed in Chapter 2.

If you wish, you can enter a description of the data in MINITAB: choose **Worksheet Description...** from the **File** menu, type the description in the **Comments** field, and click on **OK**.

If you want more practice at entering data into new worksheets, simply find a data set (from M248 or elsewhere) and try it yourself!

To end this chapter a few hints and tips on entering data are given below.

◇ If the entry direction arrow is pointing down, then pressing the **Home** key makes the cell at the top of the current column active and pressing the **End** key makes the cell containing the last (bottom) entry in the column the active cell. If the entry direction arrow is pointing right, then pressing the **Home** key makes the cell in the first column of the current row the active cell, and pressing the **End** key makes the cell containing the last (rightmost) entry in the row the active cell.

◇   When entering larger data sets where the whole data set cannot be seen in the window at once, you can use the scroll bars to change the part of the worksheet that you can see in the window, and then click in the cell where you want to enter or edit data.

◇   The row and column headings in a worksheet window do not scroll when the data scrolls, so it is surprisingly easy to start entering the next column (or row) of data in the wrong place. What happens is as follows. You enter the first column of data, pressing **Enter** after each value to move on to the next cell. When you get to the bottom of the window, it scrolls automatically. Thus, if there are (say) 20 values in the column, by the time you finish entering the column, the top row that is visible in the window might be row 10, say (the row number will depend on the window size). You then click in the top cell that is visible in the second column to start entering the second column of data — but it is not really the first row of the column, it is row 10; and so the data value is entered in the wrong row. (MINITAB fills up the cells at the top of the column with 'missing value' symbols, *, which is almost certainly not what you intend!) One way to avoid this is to routinely use the **Home** key to return to the top of the column you have just entered. Then use the **Tab** or right arrow key to move to the next column.

◇   Suppose you want to enter a data set with a text column describing the categories into which particular individuals fall. There may be only a few categories. For instance, in the data on tattoo removals in Table 1.7 of *Unit A1*, there were only two Depth categories: 'deep' and 'moderate'. It is tedious to type 'deep' or 'moderate' in full in every row of the worksheet. You can avoid doing this by using numeric codes: here you might use 1 for 'deep' and 2 for 'moderate'. Then click on **Data**, move the mouse pointer to **Code** and choose **Numeric to Text...** from the **Code** submenu that appears. The **Code - Numeric to Text** dialogue box allows you to create a new column from the column of depth codes (1s and 2s), in which the 1s are replaced by the word 'deep' and the 2s by the word 'moderate'. In this way you only have to type 'deep' once and 'moderate' once!

Summary of Chapter 6

In this chapter you have seen how to enter data from the keyboard into a blank MINITAB worksheet. Some hints on entering data have also been given.

Chapter 7
Probability models

The second component of the software for M248, which is called SUStats (*Software for Understanding Statistics*), consists of programs designed specifically to help develop your understanding and appreciation of a range of statistical concepts. In this chapter, you will use four of these programs to explore further the settling-down phenomenon that was discussed in Section 1 of *Unit A3*.

The probability that an event E occurs in a single experiment is defined to be the value towards which the sample relative frequency for the event E tends in a long sequence of repetitions of the experiment. The first program that you will use is designed to allow you to explore further the situation described in Activity 1.1 of *Unit A3*, in which a die is rolled repeatedly and the proportion of rolls that result in either a 3 or a 6 is noted after each roll. In Subsection 2.1 of *Unit A3*, the idea of a random variable was introduced and the distinction between discrete and continuous random variables was discussed. You will use the other three programs to explore what probability models for three different random variables might look like; two of these random variables are discrete and the other is continuous.

Computer Activity 7.1   Running SUStats

Click on the **Start** button, move the mouse pointer to **All Programs** (or **Programs**), then to **M248**, and click on **SUStats**.

The programs are arranged according to the unit in which they are first used. To select a program, first select the tab corresponding to the unit you are studying (by clicking on it). If there is no tab for a unit, then this means that there are no programs for that unit.

When the tab for a unit is selected, a button for each of the programs associated with the unit is displayed on the screen. Try switching between groups of programs (by clicking on the tabs) to see what programs are available.

A program is started by clicking on its button.

You can exit from SUStats at any time by clicking on the **Exit** button.

In Activity 1.1 of *Unit A3*, you were invited to roll a die 30 times and, after each roll, record the proportion of rolls that had resulted in either a 3 or a 6. It was observed that this proportion (the sample relative frequency for a 3 or a 6) appeared to be settling down to a value of about $\frac{1}{3}$, but with only 30 rolls we could not be absolutely sure of this: we really needed to carry out a much longer sequence of rolls of the die. No doubt you found rolling a die and recording the outcome soon became tedious, even for as few as 30 rolls, so you certainly would not want to roll a die as many as (say) 300 times.

Fortunately, the computer can help with this sort of task. Of course, the computer does not actually roll a die. But, when programmed appropriately, it produces results that are indistinguishable from what might occur if a die were rolled. In Computer Activity 7.2, you will use the first of the programs for *Unit A3* to mimic rolling a die a large number of times to see what might happen if you actually rolled the die repeatedly. This sort of alternative to carrying out a real experiment is known as **simulation**.

Computer Activity 7.2   Settling down

(a) Click on the tab for *Unit A3*, then click on the **Rolling a die** button to start this program.

The program is designed to simulate the experiment described in Activity 1.1 of *Unit A3*. The controls for the simulation are on the left-hand side of the **Rolling a die** window. When the simulation is run, the results are displayed on the right.

When the program is started, the simulation is in **Self select** mode and, unless you change the settings, the number of rolls in a simulation is 30. You will see a spinning die at the bottom of the screen. The die is not spinning randomly, but each of the six faces is displayed in turn in the order $1, 2, \ldots, 6$.

◇ Click on the **Stop** button.

The die will stop spinning and a success will be recorded if the face showing is numbered either 3 or 6, or a failure if any other face is showing. The proportion of successes obtained so far is plotted on the graph and displayed in the **Proportion** box under the graph. Although the die is not spinning randomly, it is spinning so rapidly that the face selected when you click on the **Stop** button is effectively random, just as the score obtained when a die is rolled is random.

Of course, after only one roll of the die the proportion is 1 if a success was recorded or 0 for a failure.

Notice that when you click on the **Stop** button, it changes to a **Start** button. Clicking on **Start** will start the die spinning again, so to simulate rolling the die several times you just need to click on the **Stop/Start** button repeatedly. After each 'roll', the proportion of successes so far is calculated and plotted on the graph. The current proportion of successes is displayed in the **Proportion** box at each stage of the simulation.

This is what you did in Activity 1.1 of *Unit A3*.

◇ Continue 'rolling the die' by clicking on the **Stop/Start** button repeatedly until you have 'rolled the die' 30 times. The **Stop/Start** button will then be disabled until you click on the **Reset** button.

◇ Click on the **Reset** button. This clears the graph and leaves the program ready for the next simulation.

◇ Click on **Start** to start the die rolling again.

◇ Run the simulation again.

Are your results similar to those you obtained when you actually rolled a die 30 times?

(b) No doubt you found clicking on the **Stop/Start** button repeatedly soon became tedious. And you certainly would not want to do so for a long simulation. You can leave it to the computer to select the faces by changing to **Auto select** mode (by clicking on it or on its radio button). Do this now. When in this mode, clicking on the **Stop/Start** button pauses and restarts a simulation. Note that in this mode you can also adjust the speed at which the simulation takes place by moving the thumb of the slider. The slider is disabled in **Self select** mode.

The thumb of the slider is moved with the mouse: place the mouse pointer on the thumb of the slider, then hold down the mouse button while moving the mouse.

◇ Now change the number of rolls of the die to 300. (Place the cursor in the **Number of rolls** field and replace 30 with 300.)

◇ Click on **Start** to begin the simulation.

Check that you can pause and restart the simulation and that you can use the slider to adjust the speed of the simulation.

Does the proportion of successes appear to be settling down to $\frac{1}{3}$?

Finally, run the simulation for a large number of rolls of your own choice. Again, does the proportion of successes appear to be settling down to $\frac{1}{3}$?

The maximum number of rolls allowed is 100 000, but that will take a long time unless you have a very fast computer!

When you have finished exploring the settling-down phenomenon, click on **Exit** to return to the list of programs for *Unit A3*.

Comment

Each time I carried out a simulation using the program, I obtained a graph with properties similar to those in Figure 1.1 of *Unit A3*: the proportion of successes appeared to be settling down towards $\frac{1}{3}$. However, the intermediate proportions varied from one simulation to the next.

Computer Activity 7.3   The score on a die ————————————

The program **Score on a die** may be used to simulate an experiment in which a perfect six-sided die is rolled a large number of times and the observed frequencies of 1s, 2s, ..., 6s (the six possible outcomes) are recorded.

(a) Click on the **Score on a die** button to start this program. As you can see, the window for this program is very similar to the window for the **Rolling a die** program: the controls are on the left-hand side and the results are displayed on the right. The main difference is that **Self select** mode is not available with this program: the computer selects the scores on the die automatically.

Initially, the program is set to roll the die 30 times.

◇ Move the slider to 'Slow' and click on **Start** to begin the simulation.

After each roll a histogram of the relative frequencies of the scores 1, 2, 3, 4, 5 and 6 is displayed on the right-hand side of the screen. Notice that for the first ten rolls the vertical scale goes up to 1, and then the vertical scale changes so that it only goes up to 0.5. When you are sure that you understand what is happening, speed up the simulation by moving the thumb of the slider.

◇   Click on **Reset**, then **Start** to run another simulation.

◇   Run several simulations with 30 rolls of the die. What do you notice about the relative frequencies in your simulations?

(b) Now change the number of rolls (the sample size) to 300 and run a simulation.

(c) Run a simulation for 3000 rolls of the die. Do not click on **Reset** when the simulation ends.

Notice that the vertical scale changes for a second time after 100 rolls and thereafter only shows values up to 0.25.

(d) Select **Combine samples** (by clicking on it or on its radio button). When this option is selected, the results of any new sample that is generated are combined with the current results. This allows you to accumulate the results from successive samples.

Change the sample size to 1000, then click on **Reset** and **Start**. The results of 1000 rolls will be combined with the results of the sample of 3000 rolls from part (c). Repeat this several times. What do you notice about the relative frequencies of the scores as the total number of rolls increases?

When you have finished exploring this situation, click on **Exit** to return to the list of programs for *Unit A3*.

Comment

This situation is discussed in Subsection 2.2 of *Unit A3*. When you have worked through this chapter, compare your observations with the comments given there on the results of simulations such as these.

Example 7.1   *Visual perception*

In an experiment on visual perception, a screen of small squares was created. The size of the screen was 27 inches by 40 inches; there were 155 520 small squares (324 by 480). A computer was used to colour each small square either black or white in such a way that, for each square, the probability that it was coloured black was equal to 0.29.

After this was done, and before performing the experiment, the screen was sampled to see whether the colouring algorithm had operated successfully. A sample of 1000 larger squares, each consisting of 16 (4 × 4) small squares, was selected and the number of black small squares in each larger square was counted.

The number of black small squares in each larger square is a random variable that can take integer values between 0 and 16 inclusive. To assess whether the colouring algorithm was operating successfully, a probability model for this random variable was needed. The data were then compared with the model. In the computer activity that follows, you will be using the program **Visual perception (1)** to simulate drawing samples of larger squares from a screen of small squares and hence discover what an appropriate model might look like. You will be revisiting this example in Chapter 9.   ◆

A suitable model is developed in Section 4 of *Unit A3*.

Computer Activity 7.4   *Looking for a probability model* _____

The sampling situation described in Example 7.1 is simulated in the program **Visual perception (1)**. The program allows you to simulate taking a sample of larger (4 × 4) squares for any sample size up to 1000, and to display a histogram showing the numbers of black small squares in the larger squares in the sample. In this activity, you will investigate what the distribution of the number of black small squares in a larger (4 × 4) square might look like; that is, you will look at the relative frequencies of larger squares containing 0, 1, 2, . . . , 16 black small squares for various sample sizes.

(a) ◇   Click on **Visual perception (1)** to start the program.

The controls for this simulation are along the bottom of the window; the results are displayed in tabbed panels. When the program is started, the panel labelled **Screen** is displayed. Each small square of the screen described in Example 7.1 is represented by a pixel. When you start the program, the computer randomly colours each of the 155 520 pixels either black or white, with the probability of black equal to 0.29.

◇   Click on **Take samples from screen**.

A sample of 50 squares each containing 16 (4 × 4) pixels is taken. These squares are coloured red on the screen. When the sample is taken, the number of black pixels in each square is recorded.

The default sample size is 50.

◇   Click on the tab labelled **n = 50** and you will see a histogram of the relative frequencies of $0, 1, \ldots, 16$.

◇   Click again on **Take samples from screen** and a second histogram will be displayed next to the first.

Each time you click on **Take samples from screen**, a sample of 50 squares is taken from the screen and a histogram is displayed on the **n = 50** panel.

Obtain a total of four samples of size 50. Comment on the similarities and differences between the histograms of the sample data.

If you take more than four samples, then the histograms will be displayed as you take the samples, with at most four in view at any time. You can view any of the other histograms by using the scroll bar.

(b)   Change the sample size to 100 and take four samples from the screen. Notice that a new panel labelled **n = 100** is created to display the histograms of samples of size 100. Again, note any similarities and differences between the histograms. Are the differences smaller or greater than for samples of size 50?

(c)   Repeat part (b) for samples of size 500.

(d)   Click on the tab labelled **Settling down**.

If you take samples while the **Settling down** panel is on top, the samples will be combined as you take them: the results are accumulated to produce one large histogram. Take a sample of size 10, then another, and several more to see how the shape of the histogram changes as the total number of squares sampled increases. Change the sample size to 100 and add several more samples, then to 1000 (say) and note how the shape of the histogram changes as more and more squares are sampled. Comment on your results.

When you have finished exploring the settling-down phenomenon, click on **Exit** *to return to the list of programs for Unit A3. If the* **Exit** *button is hidden behind your Windows taskbar, then click on the cross in the top right-hand corner of the window instead.*

Comment

For samples of size 50, there is considerable variation in the shapes of the histograms for different samples although, roughly speaking, the relative frequencies for intermediate numbers of black pixels in a square are greater than those for small or large numbers of black pixels. For samples of size 100, there is less variation between samples than for samples of size 50. For samples of size 500, there is less variation than for samples of size 100, although it is still not clear, for instance, what is the most likely number of black pixels in a square.

When using the **Settling down** panel to accumulate the results from successive samples, it is clear that the shape of the histogram is settling down as more and more squares are sampled. It looks as though four black pixels is the most likely number of black pixels in a square, being slightly more likely than five, and much more likely than any of the other numbers. A probability model suitable for describing the variation in the number of black pixels in a square is developed in Section 4 of *Unit A3*. This situation is investigated further in Chapter 9 of this computer book.

Chapter 9 is associated with Unit A4.

You have now used three programs to explore the settling-down phenomenon that underpins the definition of probability. Computer Activities 7.3 and 7.4 involved discrete random variables—the score on a die and the number of black small pixels in a 4 by 4 square, respectively. You have seen how, for very large samples, the shape of a histogram varies very little from sample to sample. So, given a very large sample, the relative frequencies of the different possible outcomes may be used to estimate the probabilities of the outcomes, thus suggesting a possible probability model for the random variable. Computer Activities 7.5 and 7.6 involve a situation where a continuous probability model is appropriate.

Computer Activity 7.5 *The weights of American adults* _____

The weights of American adults vary from one individual to another, so the weight of a randomly selected adult American may be modelled by a random variable.

Although in practice weights can be recorded only as accurately as the scales used, weights can take any value in an interval of values, so a continuous model is needed. In this activity, you will investigate what a continuous model for the weights of adult Americans might look like.

The data on which the program **American weights** is based are from the third National Health and Nutrition Examination Survey (NHANES III). The program may be used to simulate taking samples of weights (in kilograms) of adult Americans from a population of such weights.

(a) ◇   Click on the **American weights** button.

As for the previous program, the controls are along the bottom and the results are displayed in tabbed panels.

The program allows you to take samples from a population of weights and display histograms of the sample data. The histograms are all scaled so that the total area of the bars is equal to 1. This means that the area of a bar in a histogram is equal to the proportion of weights in the sample that are in the interval of weights represented by that bar.

The default sample size is 500. Take four samples of size 500. Comment on the shapes of the histograms.

(b)   Change the sample size to 5000 and take four samples of size 5000. Again, comment on the shapes of the histograms. Notice that since the sample size is much larger than that in part (a), narrower intervals have been used when drawing the histograms, thus providing more information about the distribution of weights in the population.

(c)   Change the sample size to 50 000 and take four samples of size 50 000. Once again, comment on the shapes of the histograms. Since the sample size is much larger than that in part (b), even narrower intervals have been used when drawing the histograms, thus providing yet more information about the distribution of weights in the population.

(d)   What do you think a model for the weights of adult Americans should look like?

Comment

For each of the sample sizes suggested, all the histograms have a single clear peak and a longer tail of values to the right of this peak than to the left. So a model for the weights of American adults should be unimodal and right-skew. For the larger sample sizes there was less variation between the shapes of the histograms; and since more intervals were used to summarize the data, more detailed information about the distribution of weights in the population could be deduced from a histogram. A possible model for the weights of adult Americans is introduced in Computer Activity 7.6.

Computer Activity 7.6 *Modelling weights* —————————————

You should still have the program **American weights** running. If not, then start it now.

Click on the tab labelled **Settling down**. This panel works in a similar way to the **Settling down** panel in the **Visual perception (1)** program. Each time a sample is taken, the results are combined with those of samples already taken while using the panel, so that the results of successive samples are accumulated.

Begin by taking a sample of size 500, then take several more samples of this size.

Increase the sample size (to 5000, say) and take several more samples. Notice how the shape of the histogram changes as each sample is added: it becomes less jagged and changes less with each additional sample as the total number of weights sampled increases.

Increase the sample size again (to 10 000, say) and keep taking samples. Notice that after a while the shape of the histogram changes very little as further results are accumulated: the shape of the histogram is settling down and most of the jaggedness which occurred when smaller numbers of weights were sampled disappears. This suggests that a smooth curve might provide an adequate model for the variation in the weights of American adults.

Click on **Add model** and a curve will be superimposed on your histogram. As you can see, this curve 'fits' the data well: the curve matches the shape of the histogram very closely. The total area under this curve is equal to 1. This means that, for example, the proportion of American adults weighing over 100 kg could be estimated by finding the area under the curve to the right of 100. The idea of using a curve to model the variation in a continuous random variable is developed further in some of the later sections of *Unit A3* and in later units of M248.

When you have finished using this program to investigate the distribution of weights, click on **Exit** to return to the list of programs for *Unit A3*, then on **Exit** to close SUStats.

Random numbers and random samples

In the activities in this chapter, you have been using programs to simulate situations involving chance. For example, you used **Rolling a die** and **Score on a die** to simulate rolling a fair six-sided die; and you used **Visual perception (1)** and **American weights** to simulate taking random samples from populations.

It may seem paradoxical to use a computer to produce 'random' values: we would expect any computer program to produce output that is entirely predictable. Nevertheless, computer 'random number generators' are in common use; these generate sequences of 'random' integers. Given an initial value — the *seed* value — the sequence generated is predictable and therefore is not truly random. However, in practice, sequences of such numbers are indistinguishable from sequences of random numbers, so they may be regarded as sequences of random numbers and used to simulate random samples for statistical simulations. If the sequence of numbers generated on any occasion is to be unpredictable, then it is important that an element of chance is involved in the choice of the seed value for the sequence. In each of these programs, the seed number is taken from the computer's clock when you start the program. This makes it extremely unlikely that the samples obtained on two different occasions will be the same.

Numbers generated in this way are called *pseudo-random numbers*.

MINITAB also uses the computer's clock to choose the seed number for generating 'random' numbers.

Summary of Chapter 7

In this chapter you have used four SUStats programs to explore the settling-down effect described in *Unit A3* and to investigate several situations involving chance. You have seen how the distribution of values obtained when samples are taken from a population settles down as the sample size increases. You have also met the idea of using a curve to model the variation in a continuous random variable.

Chapter 8
The binomial distribution

In MINITAB, values of the probability function and the cumulative distribution function may be obtained for a number of families of distributions. This is done using **Probability Distributions** from the **Calc** menu. The use of MINITAB to find binomial probabilities will be illustrated using an example discussed in *Unit A3*.

Example 8.1   *Multiple choice examination scores*

An examination consists of twenty multiple choice questions. For each question, the correct answer is one of five options. The random variable T, which denotes the number of correct answers obtained by a student who guesses answers at random, has a binomial distribution: $T \sim B(20, 0.2)$. In the next three activities you will use MINITAB to find some probabilities associated with this situation. ♦

This is the situation discussed in Example 4.8 of *Unit A3*.

Computer Activity 8.1   *Pass or fail?* ─────────────────

In this activity you will use MINITAB to find the following probabilities for a student who guesses answers at random in the multiple choice examination just described.

1   The probability that the student scores exactly 10 and so just passes the examination.

2   The probability that the student fails the examination.

(a) ◇   Click on **Calc** and move the mouse pointer to **Probability Distributions** so that the contents of this submenu are displayed.

Three groups of distributions are listed in the submenu. The first group contains the names of several commonly used continuous probability models; you will meet most of these in M248. The third group also consists of continuous probability models. The second group contains discrete probability models; the binomial distribution is the first one listed.

◇   Choose **Binomial...** from the submenu, and the **Binomial Distribution** dialogue box will open. This is shown in Figure 8.1.

If you have already used **Binomial...** in your current MINITAB session, then the settings may be different and some of the fields may contain values.

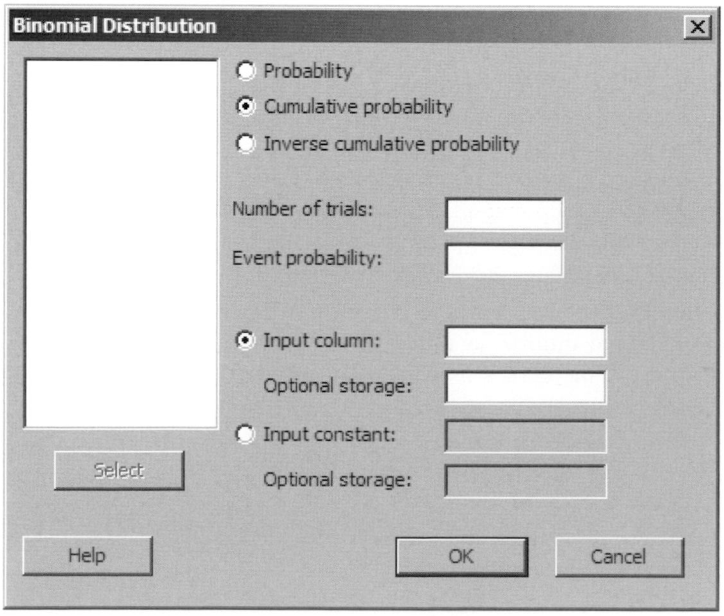

Figure 8.1   The **Binomial Distribution** dialogue box

This dialogue box requires you to do three things.

◇ Specify whether you require a value of the p.m.f. (**Probability**), the c.d.f. (**Cumulative probability**) or an **Inverse cumulative probability**.

◇ Specify values for the parameters of the distribution.

◇ Indicate which probability or probabilities you want to find, and (optionally) where to store the results.

The **Inverse cumulative probability** option is discussed in Chapter 13.

(b) The first probability required is $P(T = 10)$, where $T \sim B(20, 0.2)$. So a value of the p.m.f. is needed.

◇ Select **Probability** by clicking on it or on its radio button.

The parameters of the binomial distribution are $n = 20$ and $p = 0.2$.

◇ Type the number 20 in the **Number of trials** field, and the value 0.2 in the **Event probability** field.

◇ A single probability is required, so select **Input constant**.

◇ Since the probability required is $P(T = 10)$, enter the value 10 in the **Input constant** field. You do not need to store this probability, so leave the **Optional storage** field empty.

◇ Click on **OK** (or press **Enter**) and the following output will be displayed in the Session window.

```
Probability Density Function
Binomial with n = 20 and p = 0.2

  x         P(X = x)
 10        0.0020314
```

So the probability that a student who guesses answers at random will obtain exactly ten correct answers in twenty questions is approximately 0.0020.

Remarks

◇ In *Unit A3*, the term probability density function is used only when referring to the probability function of a continuous random variable; the probability function of a discrete distribution is called the probability mass function. However, notice that MINITAB includes the word 'Density' in the heading in the output for both discrete and continuous distributions.

◇ MINITAB always refers to the random variable in a calculation as X.

◇ The value of the parameter p must be entered as a decimal; MINITAB does not accept fractions such as $\frac{1}{6}$ for parameter values.

◇ If you want to store the result of a calculation then, *before* clicking on **OK** in the dialogue box, you must specify where it is to be stored — for example, in the constant K1 or A or whatever. This is done by typing the name of the constant in the **Optional storage** field. In this case, the result will not be displayed in the Session window. However, you can see the result by opening the Project Manager window and clicking on the **Constants** folder in the left-hand panel of the Project Manager window.

(c) The second probability required is the probability of obtaining fewer than ten correct answers, that is $P(T < 10)$, where $T \sim B(20, 0.2)$. The c.d.f. $F(.)$ of a random variable T is defined by

$$F(t) = P(T \le t).$$

So the probability required is

$$P(T < 10) = P(T \le 9) = F(9).$$

◇ Obtain the **Binomial Distribution** dialogue box. Notice that the dialogue box contains the settings from the previous calculation.

◇ Select **Cumulative probability**.

Calc > Probability Distributions > Binomial...

The parameter values $n = 20$ and $p = 0.2$ do not need to be changed. However, the probability $P(T \leq 9)$ is required.

◇   Change the value in the **Input constant** field to 9.

◇   Click on **OK**.

You should obtain the following output in the Session window.

Cumulative Distribution Function

Binomial with n = 20 and p = 0.2

  x   P(X <= x)

  9   0.997405

So the probability that a student who guesses answers at random will fail the examination is approximately 0.9974.

Computer Activity 8.2   Retake or resit?

(a) Suppose that students have to retake the module the following year if they answer fewer than four questions out of twenty correctly. What is the probability that a student who guesses answers at random has to retake the module?

(b) Students who fail the examination (that is, score less than 10) are allowed to resit the examination without retaking the whole module if they answer at least four out of the twenty questions correctly. What is the probability that a student who guesses answers at random fails and is allowed to resit the examination?

Computer Activity 8.3   Obtaining a table of results

In this activity, you will obtain a table similar to Table 4.1 of *Unit A3*, containing values of the p.m.f. and the c.d.f. for the binomial distribution $B(20, 0.2)$. If you store your results in the worksheet, then values of the p.m.f. and the c.d.f. can be displayed in a single table. To do this, you need to enter the values for which you require probabilities in a column of the worksheet *before* opening the **Binomial Distribution** dialogue box.

Enter the numbers $0, 1, 2, \ldots, 20$ in column C1 of the worksheet. You can do this either by typing in the numbers directly or as described below using **Make Patterned Data** from the **Calc** menu.

◇   Click on **Calc**, then move the mouse pointer to **Make Patterned Data**; a submenu will be displayed.

◇   Choose **Simple Set of Numbers...** from this submenu and a dialogue box will open.

◇   To store the numbers in column C1, type C1 in the **Store patterned data in** field.

◇   All the integers from 0 to 20 are required, so enter 0 in the **From first value** field and 20 in the **To last value** field. The other fields should each contain default values of 1. (If by any chance they do not, then change the values to 1 in these fields.)

◇   Click on **OK** and the numbers will be stored in column C1.

Values of the p.m.f. can be entered in column C2 as follows.

◇   Obtain the **Binomial Distribution** dialogue box.

◇   Select **Probability**.

◇   The parameters $n = 20$ and $p = 0.2$ should still be set from the previous activity; if they are not, then enter these values.

◇   Select **Input column** and type C1 in its field.

◇   Now type C2 in the **Optional storage** field and click on **OK**. The results will be stored in column C2 of the worksheet.

Calc > Probability Distributions > Binomial...

C1 is the column where you stored the values for which probabilities are required.

Values of the c.d.f. can be entered in column C3 in a similar way.

◇ Obtain the **Binomial Distribution** dialogue box.

◇ Select **Cumulative probability** and type C3 in the **Optional storage** field. (There is no need to change any of the other settings.)

◇ Click on **OK** and the results will be stored in column C3 of the worksheet.

Comment

Using this procedure, you should obtain the table of values shown in Table 8.1.

Compare the values of the c.d.f. in Table 8.1 with those in Table 4.1 of *Unit A3*. You will see that, correct to four decimal places, some of the values differ by one in the fourth decimal place. For example, in Table 4.1 of *Unit A3*, the value given for $P(T \leq 1)$ is 0.0691, whereas in this table the value given for $P(T \leq 1)$ is 0.06918, which is 0.0692 to four decimal places. This discrepancy is due to rounding error; this occurred when summing the values of the probabilities $P(T = 0)$ and $P(T = 1)$ in Table 4.1 to obtain the value given for $P(T \leq 1)$. This type of discrepancy occurs occasionally in probability calculations involving rounding and may be ignored.

Computer Activities 8.4 and 8.5 will provide you with practice at finding binomial probabilities. Use MINITAB to do the calculations.

Computer Activity 8.4   *Multiple choice tests*

(a) A test consists of ten multiple choice questions, each of which has eight options. A student must answer at least five of the questions correctly to pass the test. Find the probability that a student who guesses answers at random just passes the examination (that is, answers exactly five questions correctly). What is the probability that such a student fails the test?

(b) In another test, there are thirty questions, each of which has four options. To pass the test a student must answer at least half of them correctly. Find the probability that a student who guesses answers at random passes the test (that is, answers at least fifteen of the questions correctly).

Computer Activity 8.5   *Defective fuses*

Fuses for use in domestic electrical appliances are packaged in bags of eight for sale to customers. The probability that any fuse is defective is 0.012.

(a) Find the probability that a randomly selected bag contains exactly one defective fuse.

(b) Find the probability that a randomly selected bag contains fewer than three defective fuses.

Table 8.1   The probability distribution of $B(20, 0.2)$

t	$P(T = t)$	$P(T \leq t)$
0	0.011529	0.01153
1	0.057646	0.06918
2	0.136909	0.20608
3	0.205364	0.41145
4	0.218199	0.62965
5	0.174560	0.80421
6	0.109100	0.91331
7	0.054550	0.96786
8	0.022161	0.99002
9	0.007387	0.99741
10	0.002031	0.99944
11	0.000462	0.99990
12	0.000087	0.99998
13	0.000013	1.00000
14	0.000002	1.00000
15	0.000000	1.00000
16	0.000000	1.00000
17	0.000000	1.00000
18	0.000000	1.00000
19	0.000000	1.00000
20	0.000000	1.00000

Summary of Chapter 8

In this chapter, you have used MINITAB to calculate probabilities involving binomial distributions. In later chapters, you will use MINITAB to calculate probabilities for other probability distributions. As you will see, the procedure is essentially the same whatever the distribution.

Chapter 9
Is the model a good fit?

In this chapter, you will explore several data sets that you have met previously. For some of the data sets, a probability model for the variation in the data is proposed; for the others, you will begin by choosing a probability model yourself. In each case, you will investigate informally whether the proposed model is a good fit for the data. You will use SUStats for the activities in this chapter. However, much of the exploration can be done using MINITAB (though not as easily). Brief instructions on how to do this are given in Chapter 10.

Run SUStats now.

Computer Activity 9.1 *Royal deaths*

Click on the tab for *Unit A4*, then click on the **Royal deaths** button to start this program.

This program is designed to simulate taking samples from a probability model for the month of death of descendants of Queen Victoria. The controls for the simulation are along the bottom of the **Royal deaths** window. Above the controls are two panels. The left-hand panel contains a histogram of the data and a probability model for the data. When the simulation is run, histograms of samples from the model are displayed in the right-hand panel.

The histogram at the top of the left-hand panel shows the months of death (January = 1, February = 2, . . . , December = 12) of 82 descendants of Queen Victoria, each of whom died of natural causes. As you can see, there were more deaths in some months than in others. Is this due to random variation and just a feature of the sample of data, or are deaths more likely to occur in some months than in others?

These data are discussed in Example 4.4 of *Unit A4*.

If a death is equally likely to occur at any time of the year, then a possible model (which ignores the unequal lengths of months) is a discrete uniform distribution on the integers 1, 2, . . . , 12. A diagram of the probability mass function for this model is shown at the bottom of the left-hand panel.

Do you think that the data could be a random sample from this uniform distribution, or is there more variation in the numbers of deaths in different months than would be likely to occur by chance? You can investigate this by taking random samples from the uniform distribution and then comparing histograms of the samples with the histogram of the data. If you find that some of the histograms are as jagged as that for the data, then this will mean that the model is a plausible one and that there is no reason to suppose that deaths are more likely to occur at some times of the year than at others: the jaggedness in the histogram of the data could simply be due to random variation. Before taking any samples, make a note of what your intuition tells you: do you think these data might be a sample from a uniform distribution?

(a) In Chapter 7, you investigated the settling-down phenomenon: you saw that, in general, histograms for small samples tend to be more jagged than those for large samples from the same population. As a first step towards investigating whether the uniform distribution is a good model for the deaths data, try running the simulation for a number of different sample sizes — say, 50, 500, 5000.

⬦ Click in the **Sample size n** field and change the number to 50, then click on **Take sample**.

A histogram for a sample of size 50 will be displayed in a tabbed panel labelled **n = 50** on the right-hand side of the screen. Repeat for the other sample sizes. (A tabbed panel will be produced for each sample size that you use.) What do you notice about how the jaggedness of the histograms changes as the sample size is increased?

(b) You will have seen that for larger sample sizes the histograms are less jagged. So if you want to compare the histogram of the data with histograms of samples from the model, then the size of the samples you take is important: you must take samples of the same size as the given set of data. In this case, samples of size 82 are required.

⋄ Change the number in the **Sample size n** field back to 82 and click on **Take sample**. A histogram of a sample of size 82 will be displayed in the right-hand tabbed panel labelled **n = 82**.

The default sample size is 82.

⋄ Click on **Take sample** several times more to obtain further samples from the uniform distribution.

A histogram of each sample will be displayed as the sample is generated. Only two histograms are visible at any time, but you can view any of the other histograms by using the scroll bar. Compare the histogram of each sample with the histogram of the data.

Do you think a discrete uniform distribution is a good fit for the data? Or are royal deaths more likely to occur in some months of the year than in others? Does your conclusion here confirm or contradict what you thought before carrying out the simulation?

When you have finished exploring this situation, click on **Exit** to return to the list of programs for *Unit A4*.

Computer Activity 9.2 *Admissions to an intensive care unit*

Click on the **Admissions to intensive care** button to start this program.

As you can see, the screen for this program is very similar to that for the **Royal deaths** program. The controls are along the bottom and above them are two panels. The left-hand panel contains a histogram of the data and a probability model for the data. When the simulation is run, histograms of samples from the model are displayed in the right-hand panel.

The histogram at the top of the left-hand panel shows the times of admission to an intensive care unit (in hours after midnight) of 254 patients. The question of interest here is whether admissions occur randomly throughout the day. That is, are admissions as likely to occur at any one time of the day as at any other? If so, then an appropriate model for the times of admission is the continuous uniform distribution $U(0, 24)$. A diagram of the probability density function for this model is shown at the bottom of the left-hand panel. In this activity, you will use the program to generate random samples from this uniform distribution; you will then be able to compare histograms of the samples with the histogram of the data. Again, before taking any samples, make a note of what your intuition tells you: do you think these data might be a sample from a uniform distribution?

These data are discussed in Example 4.5 of *Unit A4*.

As before, the sample size is important. To make a valid comparison, you must take samples of the same size as the data set: 254, in this case. It is also important to use the same groupings as for the histogram of the data, because the width of the intervals used will affect the jaggedness of a histogram. The same groupings are used for the data and for the histograms of the samples in this program.

Generate several samples of size 254. Compare the histograms of the samples with the histogram of the data. Do you think the uniform distribution is a good fit for the data? Or are admissions more likely to occur at some times of the day than at others?

Note that the default sample size is 254.

When you have finished exploring this situation, click on **Exit** to return to the list of programs for *Unit A4*.

In Chapter 7, a situation was described in which it was necessary to create a screen of small squares and, at random, to colour the squares black or white. This situation is recreated in the program **Visual perception (2)**. In the program each pixel represents a small square. In Computer Activities 9.3 to 9.5, you will investigate whether the algorithm used in the program to colour the pixels black or white is operating successfully.

See Example 7.1 and Computer Activity 7.4.

Computer Activity 9.3   Visual perception — a model

In the experiment on visual perception, the size of the screen was 324×480 squares, so there were $155\,520$ small squares to colour. A computer was used to decide for each square whether it should be coloured black or white. The algorithm was designed so that decisions were made as if they were part of a long sequence of independent Bernoulli trials with the predetermined probabilities $P(\text{black}) = 0.29$ and $P(\text{white}) = 0.71$.

Before the experiment was carried out, a check was made on whether the colouring algorithm had operated successfully. A total of 1000 larger squares each consisting of 16 (4×4) small squares were selected and the number of black small squares in each larger square was counted.

Assuming that the algorithm was operating successfully, suggest a model for the number of black small squares in a larger (4×4) square.

Computer Activity 9.4   Investigating the colouring algorithm

(a) Click on the **Visual perception (2)** button to start this program.

This program is designed to simulate generating a screen of black and white squares as just described and to take samples of 1000 larger (4×4) squares from the screen. It also allows you to take samples from a probability model for the number of black small squares in each larger (4×4) square. Histograms of these samples can then be compared with a histogram of the screen data.

There are two tabbed panels in this program, labelled **Screen** and **Model**. The controls for the simulation are on the panels. Initially, the **Screen** panel is on top. This panel shows a screen consisting of $155\,520$ pixels. Each pixel represents a small square. When you start the program, each of the pixels on the screen is coloured black or white in such a way that the probability that each pixel is black is equal to 0.29 (assuming the colouring algorithm is working correctly). If you click on **Recreate screen** then the algorithm is executed again: each pixel is again coloured either black or white to create a new screen of black and white pixels. Try this now.

◇ Now click on **Take sample of 1000 squares**. A sample of 1000 larger (4×4) squares will be taken.

◇ Switch to the **Model** panel by clicking on the tab labelled **Model**.

You will see that a histogram of the number of black pixels in each of the larger (4×4) squares is displayed at the top of the left-hand side of the **Model** panel. Below this is a diagram of the probability function of a binomial distribution with parameters $n = 16$ and $p = 0.29$.

Compare the model with the histogram of the screen data. Do you think the binomial model is a good fit for the data? You can investigate this by generating samples of size 1000 from the binomial distribution and comparing histograms for the samples with the histogram of the screen data.

◇ Click on **Take sample of size 1000 from model**. A histogram of the sample data will be displayed on the right-hand side of the panel.

Take several more samples. As for the previous programs, a histogram of each sample is displayed as the sample is generated. Only two histograms are visible at any time, but you can view any of the other histograms by using the scroll bar. Compare the histogram of each sample with the histogram of the screen data. Do the results you obtain suggest that the binomial distribution is a good model for the screen data? That is, does the colouring algorithm appear to be working satisfactorily?

(b) The program can be used to investigate whether the colouring algorithm operates successfully for values of p other than 0.29.

◇   Click on the tab labelled **Screen**.

You can specify a value for the probability that each pixel is coloured black by typing a value between 0 and 1 in the field for p. Try this now for $p = 0.6$ (say) or for a value of your own choice.

Click on **Recreate screen**, then on **Take sample of 1000 squares**, and then use the **Model** panel to take samples from the corresponding binomial model (which is $B(16, 0.6)$ if you use the value 0.6 for p). Compare the histograms of samples from the model with the histogram of the screen data as you did in part (a).

Do you think the binomial model is a good fit for the screen data and hence that the colouring algorithm is operating successfully?

Computer Activity 9.5   *Fitting a binomial model*

Now suppose that you have a screen of black and white squares generated using the colouring algorithm, that you want to investigate whether the algorithm is operating successfully, but that you do not know the value of p that was used. The **Visual perception (2)** program may also be used to investigate this situation.

(a) ◇   On the **Screen** panel, click on **Unknown p** (or on its radio button).

◇   Now click on **Recreate screen**.

The screen will be recreated for a value of p between 0 and 1 selected at random by the computer. The value of p used will not be displayed.

◇   Click on **Take sample of 1000 squares**.

As before, a sample of 1000 larger (4×4) squares will be taken. Values will be displayed in two boxes under the screen. These are labelled **Mean** and **Estimated p**. The value in the box labelled **Mean** is obtained by dividing the total number of black pixels in the 1000 squares by 1000 to find the mean number of black pixels in a 4×4 square. An estimate of the value of p that was used to generate the screen is then found by dividing this by 16. This number is the proportion of pixels that are black in the sample of 1000 squares; its value is displayed in the **Estimated p** box.

◇   Click on the tab labelled **Model**.

As before, a histogram is displayed showing the numbers of black small squares in the 1000 larger (4×4) squares in the sample.

If the algorithm is operating successfully, then these counts form a sample of size 1000 from the binomial distribution, $B(16, p)$. But p is unknown, so what value of p should be used in the model? The common-sense value to use is the estimate of p obtained from the screen data. A diagram of the probability function of a binomial distribution with parameters $n = 16$ and this estimated value for p is displayed below the histogram of the screen data.

Compare the model with the histogram of the screen data. Do you think the binomial model is a good fit for the data? You can investigate this by generating samples of size 1000 from the binomial distribution and comparing histograms for the samples with the histogram of the screen data.

◇   Click on **Take sample of size 1000 from model**. A histogram of the
sample data will be displayed on the right-hand side of the panel.

Take several more samples. As before, a histogram of each sample will be
displayed as the sample is generated. Compare the histogram of each sample
with the histogram of the screen data. Do the results you obtain suggest that
the binomial distribution is a good model for the screen data? That is, does
the colouring algorithm appear to be working satisfactorily?

◇   Click on the tab labelled **Screen** to return to the screen panel.

◇   Click on **Known p** (or on its radio button) and the value of p that was
used to create the screen will be displayed.

Is the estimate of p obtained from the sample of screen data close to the
value of p used to create the screen?

(b)   Click on **Unknown p** and then repeat the activity in part (a) at least once
more. Again, does the binomial model seem to be a good fit for the screen
data? Is the colouring algorithm working satisfactorily?

When you have completed your investigation click on **Exit** to return to the
list of programs for *Unit A4*.

Computer Activity 9.6   *Fitting normal models*

(a)   The final activity in this chapter uses the program **Normal models**. Start
this program now by clicking on its button.

Initially, the panel labelled **Scottish chests** is on top. A histogram of the
data on the chest measurements of Scottish soldiers is shown in the top left
corner of the panel. The histogram is scaled so that the total area of the bars
is equal to 1. The mean and standard deviation of the data are given below
the histogram, followed by the panel controls.

These data were discussed
briefly in Example 6.3 of
Unit A3.

The tabbed panels are all very similar, but each panel uses a different data
set. For each data set a normal model has been suggested in either *Unit A3*
or *Unit A4*. In this activity you will be fitting a normal model to some of the
data sets, taking samples from the model and comparing histograms of the
sample data with the original data.

The sample mean of the chest measurements (in inches) is 39.8 and the
sample standard deviation is 2.07. So a possible normal model for the chest
measurements of Scottish soldiers might have parameters $\mu = 39.8$ and
$\sigma = 2.07$, say.

◇   Type 39.8 in the field for μ and 2.07 in the field for σ.

◇   Now click on **Add normal curve**.

The probability density function for a normal distribution with mean 39.8
and standard deviation 2.07 will be superimposed on the histogram of the
data. Does it look as though this distribution is a good model for the
variation in chest measurements?

As in the earlier activities in this chapter, you can investigate the fit of a
model by generating samples of the same size as the data set and comparing
histograms of the samples with the histogram of the data.

◇   Click on **Take sample from model**.

A sample of the same size as the data set (5732) will be taken and a
histogram of the sample data (using the same groupings as for the data set)
will be displayed on the right-hand side of the panel.

Take several samples and compare their histograms with the histogram of the
data. Do you think that this normal model fits the data well?

You can view any of the
histograms by using the scroll
bar.

(b) Data on the heights in centimetres of 351 elderly women were given in Example 6.1 of *Unit A3*. You can investigate whether a normal model is a good fit for these data using the panel labelled **Heights**.

   ◇   Click on the tab labelled **Heights**.

   As you can see, this panel is similar in design to the one for chest measurements. Use it to investigate whether a normal model is a good fit for the data.

(c) Data on the blood plasma β nicotine levels of 55 smokers were given in Example 6.2 of *Unit A3*. Investigate whether a normal model is a good fit for these data using the panel labelled **Nicotine levels**.

(d) *Optional activity*   Data on the maximum head breadth of samples of Etruscan skulls and modern Italian skulls were given in Example 1.1 of *Unit A4*. Using the panels labelled **Etruscan skulls** and **Italian skulls**, investigate whether normal models fit these data well.

Summary of Chapter 9

In this chapter you have investigated informally the fit of uniform models, binomial models and normal models to data. For each data set, you did this by taking samples from a proposed model and comparing histograms of the samples with a histogram of the data. You saw that in order to make a fair comparison, you must take samples of the same size as the data set, since the jaggedness of the histogram for a sample depends on the sample size. For each data set, the same groupings were used for the histograms of the samples as for the histogram of the data, since the jaggedness of a histogram also depends on the groupings used.

When fitting a normal model, you chose a normal distribution with parameters either equal to or approximately equal to the mean and standard deviation of the data. You also investigated the fit of a binomial model in a situation where the parameter p was estimated from the data.

Later in M248, you will meet a formal statistical method for testing the goodness of fit of a model to data.

Chapter 10
Investigating the fit using MINITAB

Many of the activities involved in investigating the fit of a model to data in Chapter 9 can be done using MINITAB, though not as easily. In this chapter, several facilities of MINITAB that are needed for this, and which have not yet been discussed, are introduced briefly. This chapter is for interest only: if you are short of time, you may leave it for now. Any MINITAB features introduced here that are used later in M248 will be described when required. You will not be able to reproduce the simulation in Computer Activities 9.4 and 9.5 as these involved producing a screen of black and white pixels. This cannot be done using MINITAB.

The data sets

The data sets used in Chapter 9 are all contained in MINITAB worksheets.

The royal deaths data of Computer Activity 9.1 are in the worksheet **royals.mtw**.

The data on the admissions to an intensive care unit of Computer Activity 9.2 are in the worksheet **icu.mtw**.

In Computer Activities 9.4 and 9.5, you investigated the colouring algorithm for a screen of black and white pixels. The data from the original experiment to investigate the operation of a screen-colouring algorithm are in the worksheet **screen.mtw**.

The data sets used in Computer Activity 9.6 are in the following worksheets: **scots.mtw**, **osteoporosis.mtw**, **plasma.mtw** and **skulls.mtw**.

Estimating the parameters of a normal model

The mean and standard deviation of a data set are included in the output for **Display Descriptive Statistics. . . .** These are the values needed to estimate the parameters of a normal model for the data.

Histograms and normal curves

A histogram with a normal curve superimposed can be obtained either using **Histogram. . .** from the **Graph** menu or using **Display Descriptive Statistics. . . .** If you wish to see how this is done, then try Computer Activity 10.1.

Computer Activity 10.1   *Producing a histogram and normal curve* ___

(a) Open the worksheet **osteoporosis.mtw**, then follow the steps below.

⬦ Obtain the **Histograms** dialogue box.

Graph > Histogram. . .

⬦ Select **With Fit** and click on **OK**.

⬦ In the **Histogram - With Fit** dialogue box, enter `height` in the **Graph variables** field.

⬦ Click on **OK**.

A histogram of the data with a normal curve superimposed will be displayed in a Graph window. Alternatively, a histogram with a normal curve superimposed can be obtained using **Display Descriptive Statistics. . .**, as follows.

⬦ Obtain the **Display Descriptive Statistics** dialogue box.

Stat > Basic Statistics > Display Descriptive Statistics. . .

⬦ The heights of the elderly women are in the column `height`, so enter `height` in the **Variables** field.

⬦ Click on the **Graphs. . .** button, then select **Histogram of data, with normal curve** in the **Display Descriptive Statistics - Graphs** dialogue box.

⬦ Click on **OK** to close this dialogue box, then click on **OK** again.

Summary statistics will be displayed in the Session window and a histogram of the data with a normal curve superimposed will be displayed in a Graph window. Whichever method you use, the parameters of the normal model will be the sample mean and the sample standard deviation of the data: you do not have the option of choosing the parameters of the normal model that is fitted. You can choose the groupings used for the histogram by editing the scale on the horizontal axis, as described in Section 3.1.

(b) The data in **scots.mtw** are in summary form. For data in this form, a histogram with a normal curve superimposed can only be produced using **Histogram. . . .** Try this now, as follows.

⬦ Obtain the **Histogram - With Fit** dialogue box.

⬦ Enter `circumference` in the **Graph variables** field.

⬦ Click on the **Data Options. . .** button to open the **Histogram - Data Options** dialogue box.

⬦ Click on the **Frequency** tab, and enter `frequency` in the **Frequency variable(s)** field of the **Frequency** panel.

⬦ Click on **OK**, then on **OK** again.

Generating random samples from a probability distribution

Samples from probability distributions are generated using **Random Data** from the **Calc** menu. After choosing a family of distributions from the **Random Data** submenu, you need to enter the following information in its dialogue box: the sample size, the columns where the sample data are to be stored and the parameters of the distribution. Note that there is an upper limit of 150 million on the number of cells per worksheet, but that entering a large number of cells of data could slow the performance of your computer significantly. The use of **Random Data** is illustrated in Computer Activity 10.2 for the discrete uniform distribution used to model the deaths data in Computer Activity 9.1.

> You can have at most 4000 columns and at most 10 million rows in a worksheet.

Computer Activity 10.2 Generating random samples from a discrete uniform distribution

Open the worksheet **royals.mtw**. Samples from a discrete uniform distribution can be generated using **Integer...** from the **Random Data** submenu of the **Calc** menu. Do this now, as follows.

> **Uniform...** in the **Random Data** submenu refers to the *continuous* uniform distribution.

◇   Choose **Integer...** from the **Random Data** submenu of **Calc**.

The first field (at the top of the dialogue box) is for specifying the number of rows of data to generate (that is, the sample size). There are 82 values in the sample of data on the months of royal deaths, so samples of size 82 are required.

◇   Enter 82 in the **Number of rows of data to generate** field.

Next, you must say where the data are to be stored by entering the name(s) of the column(s) in the **Store in column(s)** field. Suppose that you wish to generate four samples of size 82 and store them in columns C3, C4, C5 and C6.

◇   Type C3-C6 in the **Store in column(s)** field.

Finally, you must enter the parameters of the distribution. For the discrete uniform distribution, you need to enter the minimum and maximum values in the range of the distribution in the fields labelled **Minimum value** and **Maximum value**. In this case, the required values are 1 and 12.

◇   Enter 1 in the **Minimum value** field and 12 in the **Maximum value** field.

◇   Click on **OK**.

Four samples of 82 random observations from a discrete uniform distribution on the integers $1, 2, \ldots, 12$ will be stored in columns C3 to C6. You can then produce histograms for these samples of data and compare them with a histogram of the royal deaths data.

Note that, when producing histograms of the data or of the random samples, you may need to choose the cutpoints or midpoints for the bars so that all the histograms use the same groupings. If different groupings are used on different histograms, this will make it difficult to compare the histograms.

Summary of Chapter 10

In this chapter, some features of MINITAB that are needed in order to carry out some of the investigations from Chapter 9 have been described. You have seen how to produce a histogram of a data set with a normal curve superimposed using either **Histogram...** or **Display Descriptive Statistics....** And you have learned how to generate random samples from probability distributions using **Random Data**.

Chapter 11
Investigating binomial distributions

In this chapter, you will use SUStats to investigate the circumstances in which a binomial distribution with parameters n and p may be approximated by a distribution that depends only on the mean $\mu = np$ of the binomial distribution—that is, by a Poisson distribution with parameter μ. This chapter begins with an example of a situation in which a binomial distribution is approximated by a Poisson distribution.

Example 11.1   V1 flying bombs

In the autumn of 1944, nearly 10 000 V1 flying bombs were launched against British towns and cities. The majority of those that got through the defences descended on London. The German propaganda claimed that the V1 bomb was an accurately aimed weapon. To investigate this claim, the London Fire Brigade plotted the positions of all the V1 hits within a 6 km by 6 km square of South London. Probability modelling was then used to investigate whether the positions where the bombs landed were randomly distributed in the square.

The 6 km by 6 km square was divided into a grid of 0.25 km by 0.25 km squares. ◆

Computer Activity 11.1   The V1 data —————————

Run SUStats now.

Click on the tab for *Unit A5*, then click on the **V1 bombs** button to start this program.

The opening panel shows a map of the 6 km by 6 km square of South London, the grid of 0.25 km by 0.25 km squares and the positions of the V1 hits.

Example 11.1 continued   V1 flying bombs

The number of V1 bombs that landed on the 576 grid squares was 537—an average of $\mu = 537/576 \simeq 0.932$ hits per grid square. The number of hits in each of these grid squares was counted. The results are summarized in Figure 11.1.

The investigators looked at whether the distribution of the number of hits in a grid square was consistent with the hits being randomly located in the large 6 km by 6 km square.

A model was required for the number of hits in a grid square. As a first step towards developing one, each grid square was subdivided into 900 'crater' squares. As suggested by the name, each of these squares was roughly the size of the crater made by a V1 bomb. No crater square within the 6 km by 6 km square of South London suffered more than one hit.

The following modelling assumptions were made.

◇ A hit at one point is no more likely than a hit at any other point. In other words, the probability that a crater square suffers a hit is constant from square to square.

◇ Where a bomb lands is not influenced in any way by where any other bomb lands. That is, whether or not a particular crater square is hit is independent of whether or not any other crater square is hit.

◇ There is a negligible chance of a bomb dropping into an existing crater. In other words, each crater square suffers at most one hit.

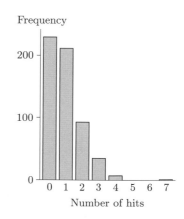

Figure 11.1 A bar chart for the number of hits in a grid square

Together these assumptions mean that the outcomes (a hit or not a hit) for the 900 crater squares in a grid square may be regarded as 900 independent Bernoulli trials with constant probability of success (a hit). So the number of hits in a grid square may be modelled by a binomial distribution with parameters $n = 900$ and $p = 0.932/900 \simeq 0.00104$. For this model, the mean number of hits per grid square is $np = 0.932$, the mean number of hits observed. This is a situation involving a binomial distribution for which the parameter p is small and n is large. ♦

In the remaining activities in this chapter, you are asked to investigate the circumstances in which a binomial distribution may be approximated by a Poisson distribution. The first of these activities (Computer Activity 11.2) concerns the modelling situation just described. You will need to use the program **V1 bombs** for all of these activities. If possible, do all three activities in one computer session.

Computer Activity 11.2   *Models for the V1 data*

(a) Click on the **V1 model** tab to obtain the second panel.

The panel shows, on a single diagram, a histogram of the V1 data and the probability function of the binomial distribution, $B(900, 0.932/900)$. As you can see, the model appears to fit the data remarkably well. So there is no reason to suppose that the bombs did not land randomly in the 6 km by 6 km square: it does not look as though the V1 bomb was an accurately aimed weapon.

(b) When developing the model, each grid square was divided into 900 (30×30) crater squares. However, a different number of crater squares might have been chosen — either fewer or more than 900. If each grid square is divided into n crater squares (instead of 900), then the corresponding model for the number of hits in a grid square is $B(n, 0.932/n)$.

By moving the thumb of the slider for n (or by typing different values for n in its field and pressing **Enter**), investigate how well the binomial model fits the data for different values of n. In particular, try to answer the following questions.

◇   For what range of values of n (approximately) does the binomial model appear to fit the data well?

◇   Describe how the binomial probabilities change as n gets larger and larger.

(c) Finally, insert a very large value of n (2000, say). Then click on the radio button labelled Poisson(0.932). The binomial probability function will be replaced on the diagram by the Poisson probability function: as you will see, the change is barely noticeable. The Poisson model also fits the data well.

Comment

The binomial model $B(n, 0.932/n)$ appears to fit the data well for values of n greater than about 50. The binomial model fits the data less and less well as n becomes smaller; and the fit is not at all good for n less than about 20.

For n greater than 50, the binomial probabilities hardly change at all as n changes.

In *Unit A5* and in Computer Activity 11.2, you have seen that, for $\mu = 1.25$ and for $\mu = 0.932$, a binomial distribution $B(n, \mu/n)$ may be approximated for large values of n by a distribution which depends only on the value of μ. This distribution is a Poisson distribution with parameter μ, and is denoted Poisson(μ). What happens for other values of μ? And how large must n be for the approximation to be a good one? You are asked to investigate these questions in Computer Activity 11.3.

Computer Activity 11.3   Good approximations ——————————

Click on the **Binomial/Poisson** tab to obtain the third panel.

The diagram shows two probability functions: one is for the binomial distribution $B(n, \mu/n)$, and the other is for the Poisson distribution with parameter μ, denoted Poisson(μ). The default values of n and μ are the values from the model used for the V1 hits: 900 and 0.932, respectively. As you can see, for these values of n and μ, the two probability functions are virtually indistinguishable on the diagram.

Move the thumb of the slider for n. Notice that the diagram of the binomial probability function changes as n changes. You investigated these changes for $\mu = 0.932$ in Computer Activity 11.1. For n greater than about 250 the two probability functions are almost indistinguishable. They differ more as n becomes smaller. But for n greater than about 50 they are still very close.

Now change the value of μ to a value of your choice. Notice that both probability functions change automatically. By moving the thumb of the slider for n (or by typing values in the field for n and pressing **Enter**), investigate how the binomial probabilities change with n. For the value of μ that you chose, write down the (approximate) range of values of n for which you consider the Poisson distribution to be a good approximation for the binomial distribution.

Remember that the binomial distribution is defined only for $\mu \leq n$, since the parameter p lies between 0 and 1 and $\mu = np$.

Repeat this investigation for a selection of different values of μ, some less than 0.932 and some greater than 0.932. Try to summarize your conclusions briefly.

Notice that for $\mu \leq 0.7$, the vertical axis goes up to 1, compared with 0.5 for $\mu > 0.7$.

Comment

For relatively large values of μ (for $\mu > 5$, say), the Poisson distribution is a good approximation for the binomial distribution only for very large values of n. For smaller values of μ, the Poisson distribution is a good approximation for a wider range of values of n.

———————————————————————

When using a binomial model, it is usual to specify the parameters n and p. Therefore, in order to be useful, any rule for the circumstances in which a Poisson approximation is good ought to be given in terms of n and p, rather than n and μ. In Computer Activity 11.4, you are asked to investigate for what ranges of values of n and of p a Poisson distribution provides a reasonable approximation for a binomial distribution. Of course, what constitutes a 'reasonable' approximation is not clear-cut. An approximation may be sufficiently good for some purposes but not for others, depending on the accuracy required. By comparing diagrams of the probability functions, you are simply being asked to try to formulate a 'rough rule' for when a Poisson approximation appears to be good. For the example discussed in Subsection 1.1 of *Unit A5*, p was small and n was fairly large. Try to find out how small p needs to be and how large n should be for a Poisson approximation to be 'good'.

Computer Activity 11.4   More on approximations ——————————

Click on the **Finding a rule** tab to obtain the fourth panel.

The diagram shows two probability functions: one is for the binomial distribution, $B(n, p)$, and the other is for the Poisson distribution, Poisson(np). The default values for n and p are 50 and 0.2, respectively. As you can see, for these values of n and p, although the shapes of the two distributions are similar, the Poisson distribution is not a very good approximation for the binomial distribution: the largest probabilities differ quite a lot.

(a)   By varying the value of n, investigate whether a Poisson distribution is ever a good approximation for the binomial distribution $B(n, p)$ when p is 0.2. If so, write down the value of n which, *in your opinion*, is the smallest for which the approximation is a good one.

(b) Repeat part (a) for successively smaller values of p; for example, 0.15, 0.12, 0.1, 0.08, and so on.

(c) Try to find a rough rule of your own involving n and p for when a Poisson distribution is a good approximation for a binomial distribution. You will shortly be able to compare this with 'our' rough rule (this is given in Subsection 1.2 of *Unit A5*).

Comment

(a) When $p = 0.2$, the Poisson distribution is not a good approximation for the binomial distribution for any value of n for which the probability functions are visible on the panel.

(b) For large values of n, the Poisson distribution provides a better approximation for the binomial distribution when $p = 0.15$ than for $p = 0.2$, but it is still not a good approximation. For the largest values of n for which the probability functions are visible on the panel, the Poisson distribution is a better approximation again when p is 0.12, but it is still not a good approximation for smaller values of n. As the value of p is reduced, the Poisson distribution provides a better and better approximation for the binomial distribution for large values of n. Also, for smaller values of p, the approximation is good for a larger range of values of n. For any particular value of p, the smallest value of n for which a Poisson distribution is a good approximation is a matter of opinion; it depends on how close you want the probabilities to be, which in turn depends on the accuracy required.

(c) You will shortly be able to compare your rough rule with one given in the unit. However, whatever your rule, the bombing situation described in Example 11.1 is likely to satisfy it: p is very small ($p \simeq 0.001$) and n is large ($n = 900$).

Note that in all these investigations you have compared only those binomial and Poisson probabilities which have the largest values. You have not compared probabilities in the tails of the distributions, where the probabilities are very small and discrepancies are difficult, if not impossible, to see. Even though, in the tails of the distributions, the absolute difference between a binomial and a Poisson probability may be extremely small, the percentage error in using the Poisson probability to approximate the binomial probability may be large. It follows that, even when you believe a Poisson distribution to be a good approximation for a binomial distribution, you should be cautious about using a Poisson approximation to calculate probabilities in the tails.

Summary of Chapter 11

In this chapter, probability modelling has been used to investigate whether the positions where V1 bombs landed within a 6 km by 6 km square of South London were random. This square was divided into 576 0.25 km by 0.25 km squares. Based on the assumption that the V1 bombs landed randomly (and hence were not accurately aimed weapons), a binomial distribution with a large value of n and a small value of p was used to model the number of hits in a grid square. You saw that the binomial model fits the data well as does a Poisson model with the same mean as the binomial model. You have used SUStats to investigate when a Poisson distribution provides a good approximation for a binomial distribution. For different values of the mean μ and of the parameters n and p of the binomial distribution, you have compared binomial distributions and Poisson distributions that have the same mean.

Chapter 12
Poisson processes

In Section 12.1 you will be given several data sets to explore. Each data set concerns events occurring in continuous time, and the purpose of your exploration will be to investigate whether or not a Poisson process might be a reasonable model for the occurrences of the events.

Section 12.2 consists of two activities in which you are asked to find probabilities associated with events occurring in a Poisson process. The use of MINITAB to do the calculations is explained.

12.1 Is a Poisson process a good model?

Data on the intervals between serious earthquakes worldwide have been discussed in *Unit A5*. In Computer Activities 12.1 and 12.2, you are asked to explore these data using MINITAB, and to reproduce some of the results and diagrams given in the unit.

Computer Activity 12.1   Is the average rate constant? _____

The data on serious earthquakes are in the worksheet **earthquakes.mtw**. Open this worksheet now.

The data are the intervals (in days) between successive serious earthquakes. In this activity you will investigate whether the rate at which serious earthquakes occurred remained constant over the period of observation. You will do this by plotting the number of earthquakes that have occurred so far against time.

(a) A serious earthquake occurred on 16 December 1902. The first entry in column C1 interval (840) is the number of days from then until the next serious earthquake. The second entry (157) is the number of days from that earthquake until the following one, and so on. Since the data are ordered, the waiting times may be added to give the times (in days after 16 December 1902) at which each earthquake occurred. For example, the second earthquake occurred 997 days (840 + 157) after 16 December 1902; that is, two earthquakes had occurred after 997 days.

MINITAB provides a function called Partial sum that can be used to calculate these times. This is one of the functions available when using Calculator... from the Calc menu.

The use of **Calculator...** was introduced in Computer Activity 3.6.

◇ Choose **Calculator...** from the **Calc** menu. The **Calculator** dialogue box will open.

◇ To store the times in a variable named time, type time in the **Store result in variable** field. (The results will be stored in the first available column, which is C2 in this case.)

Next you must enter the formula for calculating these times in the **Expression** field.

◇ Scroll through the list of functions until you come to Partial sum. Click on it to select it.

◇ Click on the **Select** button and PARS(number) will be entered in the **Expression** field. The word number will be highlighted.

◇ Type C1 to replace number by C1 (to indicate that you want to find the partial sums of the numbers in column C1).

◇ Finally, click on **OK** and the partial sums will be stored in column C2 of your worksheet.

(b) Now create a column named `number` giving the number of earthquakes that
    had occurred after each of the times in column `C2`; that is, a column
    containing the numbers $1, 2, \ldots, 62$ in that order. The quickest way to do this
    is by using **Simple Set of Numbers. . . .** (The use of **Simple Set of
    Numbers. . .** was described in Computer Activity 8.3.)

**Calc > Make Patterned
Data > Simple Set of
Numbers. . .**

(c) Obtain a scatterplot of the number of earthquakes (**Y variables**) against
    time (**X variables**). You should obtain a diagram like the one in
    Figure 12.1. (Use **Scatterplot. . .** from the **Graph** menu.)

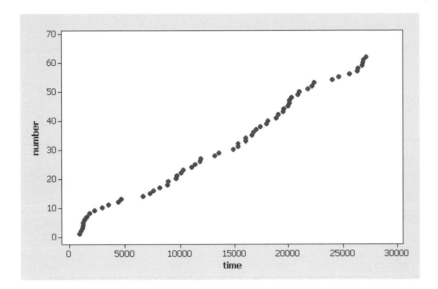

Figure 12.1   A scatterplot for the earthquakes data

As observed in the unit, the points lie quite close to a straight line through
the origin, suggesting that the rate of occurrence of serious earthquakes
remained constant over the period of observation.

Computer Activity 12.2   *Waiting times*

The intervals, or waiting times, between successive events in a Poisson process are
exponentially distributed. In this activity, you will explore the data in
earthquakes.mtw to see whether an exponential model is a good one for the
intervals between serious earthquakes.

(a) Find the mean and standard deviation of the intervals between serious
    earthquakes. Check that these values are consistent with the data being
    observations from an exponential distribution.

(b) Obtain a histogram of the data with the following properties.

    ◇   The ticks on the horizontal axis are at the cutpoints.

    ◇   The groups have width 100.

    ◇   The first group starts at 0 and the last finishes at 2000.

Use **Histogram. . .** from the
Graph menu. Its use was
introduced in Chapter 3.

Note that since waiting times
cannot be negative, the first
group must not extend below 0.

Is the shape of the histogram consistent with an exponential distribution
being a good model for the intervals between serious earthquakes?

In Computer Activity 12.1, you saw that the average rate of occurrence of serious
earthquakes appears to have remained constant over the period of observation;
and in Computer Activity 12.2, you found that an exponential distribution seems
to be a reasonable model for the intervals between serious earthquakes. These
results are consistent with a Poisson process being a reasonable model for the
occurrences of serious earthquakes.

Computer Activity 12.3   *Coal-mining explosions* ──────────

The worksheet **coal.mtw** contains data on the intervals in days between
explosions in coal mines from 15 March 1851 to 22 March 1962 inclusive. There
were 191 explosions altogether, including those on each of the two dates above. So
the worksheet contains 190 waiting times. There is one zero: two explosions
occurred on 6 December 1875.

Jarrett, R.G. (1979) A note on
the intervals between
coal-mining disasters.
Biometrika, **66**, 191–193.

In this activity, you should use the methods of Computer Activities 12.1 and 12.2
to investigate whether a Poisson process might be a good model for the
occurrences of coal-mining explosions.

(a) First, investigate whether an exponential distribution is a good model for the
intervals between coal-mining explosions.

◇   Find the mean and standard deviation of the waiting times between
explosions.

◇   Produce a histogram of the data with the first group beginning at 0 and
with groups of width 100.

Using your results, explain whether or not you think an exponential model is
a good one for the intervals between coal-mining explosions.

(b) Produce a scatterplot of the number of explosions against time.

Do you think the rate of occurrence of coal-mining explosions remained
constant over the period of observation?

Follow the method outlined in
Computer Activity 12.1.

(c) Use your answers to parts (a) and (b) to explain whether or not you think a
Poisson process is a suitable model for the occurrences of coal-mining
explosions during the period of observation.

You have now explored two data sets consisting of waiting times between events.
You have seen that the data on times between earthquakes are consistent with a
Poisson process being a good model for the occurrences of serious earthquakes.
However, you found that there is good reason to doubt that the occurrences of
coal-mining explosions may be modelled by a Poisson process: the rate of
occurrence appears to have declined over the period of observation.

Of course, if the rate of occurrence of events remains constant over time, this does
not necessarily mean that a Poisson process is a good model for the occurrences of
the events. Consider, for instance, the simple situation where events occur at
regular intervals: the events are completely predictable, and their rate of
occurrence is constant. But, if the rate remains constant and the events are
unpredictable, is a Poisson process necessarily a good model? In Computer
Activities 12.4 and 12.5 you are asked to investigate this using a data set
concerning failures of a computer system. Try to work through both activities in
the same MINITAB session.

Computer Activity 12.4   *The average rate of failures* ──────────

The data in the worksheet **dec20.mtw** relate to a DEC-20 computer that was in
use at the Open University during the 1980s. They give the number of times that
the computer broke down in each of 128 consecutive weeks of operation. (The first
entry is for the first week, the second is for the second week, and so on.)

Produce a scatterplot of the cumulative number of failures (**Y variables**) against
time (**X variables**) as follows.

◇   First create a column named **number** which contains the cumulative number
of breakdowns after each week.

◇   Now create a column named **time** which contains the week numbers
$(1, 2, \ldots, 128)$.

Use **Partial sum**, as described
in Computer Activity 12.1.

◇   Use the data in these two columns to produce the scatterplot.

What does this scatterplot tell you about the rate of occurrence of breakdowns?

Computer Activity 12.5   The number of failures in a week _____

If a Poisson process is a good model for the occurrences of failures of the computer described in Computer Activity 12.4, then the numbers of failures in a week are observations from a Poisson distribution. In this activity, you will investigate whether a Poisson distribution is a good model for the data.

You should still have the worksheet **dec20.mtw** open.

(a) Find the sample mean and sample standard deviation of the data. What can you deduce from these values?

(b) Obtain a histogram of the data, and edit the scale so that the bins have width 1.

(c) A diagram of the probability mass function of a discrete probability distribution can be obtained using **Probability Distribution Plot...** from the **Graph** menu. Obtain a diagram of the probability mass function of a Poisson distribution with mean 4.016 (the value of the sample mean), as follows.

 ◇   Choose **Probability Distribution Plot...** from the **Graph** menu.

 ◇   In the **Probability Distribution Plots** dialogue box, select **View Single** and click on **OK**.

 ◇   In the **Probability Distribution Plot - View Single** dialogue box, choose **Poisson** from the **Distribution** drop-down list, and enter 4.016 in the **Mean** field.

 ◇   Click on **OK** to obtain the diagram.

Compare your histogram of the data with the diagram of the Poisson probability mass function. Do you think the Poisson distribution is a good model for the number of failures in a week? Is a Poisson process a suitable model for the occurrences of failures?

12.2   Probability calculations

Two distributions are used when calculating probabilities associated with events occurring in a Poisson process: the Poisson distribution and the exponential distribution. The number of events that occur in an interval of length t has a Poisson distribution with parameter λt, where λ is the rate of occurrence of the events; and the waiting time between successive events has an exponential distribution with parameter λ.

As you have already seen for the binomial and Poisson distributions, probabilities are found in MINITAB using **Probability Distributions** from the **Calc** menu. When you select a family of distributions from the **Probability Distributions** submenu, a dialogue box will be opened. The only part of the dialogue box that varies from one family to another is the central part, where you specify which member of the family is required. In Chapter 8, you saw that for a binomial distribution, you must specify the **Number of trials** (n) and the **Event probability** (p). And in Computer Activity 12.5, you had to specify the **Mean** of a Poisson distribution.

Recall that the mean of a Poisson distribution with parameter μ is equal to μ.

As you will see when you try the activities in this section, for an exponential distribution, you must specify the *mean* of the distribution. Take care when using **Exponential...**. Remember that the mean of an exponential distribution is *not* the same as the parameter: if the parameter is λ, then the mean is $1/\lambda$. MINITAB requires you to enter values in two fields named **Scale** and **Threshold**. For an exponential distribution, the value in the **Threshold** field should be 0 (the default value), and the value in the **Scale** field should be the mean. (Entering a non-zero value in the **Threshold** field specifies a distribution which has the same shape as an exponential distribution, but a different range.)

The following activities serve two purposes. First, they will give you the opportunity to ensure that you can use MINITAB to find probabilities involving exponential distributions and Poisson distributions. Secondly, they will provide you with practice at deciding what probabilities are required in questions about Poisson processes.

Computer Activity 12.6 Serious earthquakes

In Computer Activities 12.1 and 12.2, you explored data on the waiting times between serious earthquakes covering the period from December 1902 until March 1977. The data appear to be consistent with a Poisson process being a reasonable model for the occurrences of serious earthquakes.

Suppose that the occurrences of serious earthquakes may be modelled by a Poisson process with rate $\lambda = 62/27107$ per day.

(a) Write down the distribution of the number of serious earthquakes that occur in a typical four-year period.

(b) Use MINITAB to find each of the following probabilities.

(i) The probability that exactly five serious earthquakes occur in a four-year period.

(ii) The probability that fewer than three serious earthquakes occur in a four-year period.

(iii) The probability that at least eight serious earthquakes occur in a four-year period.

(c) Write down the distribution of the waiting time between serious earthquakes. Calculate the mean waiting time to the nearest day.

(d) Use MINITAB to find the probability that the gap between successive serious earthquakes

(i) will be less than 30 days;

(ii) will exceed two years.

Computer Activity 12.7 Emissions of alpha particles

In Example 3.6 of *Unit A5*, you saw that the Poisson distribution is a good fit for the data given on the numbers of particles emitted from a radioactive source in $7\frac{1}{2}$-second intervals.

Suppose that emissions of alpha particles may be modelled by a Poisson process with rate $\lambda = 0.517$ per second. (This is the estimate for λ obtained from the data.)

(a) Write down the distribution of the number of alpha particles emitted in a one-minute period.

(b) (i) Find the probability that exactly 30 particles are emitted in a one-minute period.

(ii) Find the probability that fewer than 20 particles are emitted in a one-minute period.

(iii) Find the probability that at least 50 particles are emitted in one minute.

(c) Write down the probability distribution of the interval between successive emissions of particles.

(d) (i) Find the probability that the interval between successive emissions is less than half a second.

(ii) Find the probability that the interval between successive emissions exceeds three seconds.

Summary of Chapter 12

In this chapter, you have used MINITAB to explore several data sets. This involved using many facilities that you have met in earlier chapters: for example, **Calculator...** and **Make Patterned Data** from the **Calc** menu, **Basic Statistics** from the **Stat** menu, and **Scatterplot...**, **Bar Chart...** and **Histogram...** from the **Graph** menu. Some features of these facilities were used for the first time: for instance, the function `Partial sum` (available using **Calculator...**) was used to find the cumulative sums of a column of numbers; and you calculated probabilities for Poisson distributions and exponential distributions using **Probability Distributions**. You also learned how to use **Bar Chart...** to create a diagram of the probability mass function of a Poisson distribution.

Chapter 13
Quantiles

You have now used **Probability Distributions** from the **Calc** menu to find probabilities for binomial, Poisson and exponential distributions. In this chapter, you will use **Probability Distributions** to find quantiles for a number of distributions, both continuous and discrete.

When you choose a family of distributions from the **Probability Distributions** submenu, a dialogue box opens. Whichever family you choose, this box requires similar information. Quantiles are values of the inverse of the cumulative distribution function; so to find quantiles, you must select **Inverse cumulative probability** from the top section of the dialogue box. In the middle section of the dialogue box, you must specify which member of the family of distributions is required. The bottom section of the box is where you specify the input and (optionally) where to store the results.

When finding quantiles, the values that you input (either using **Input column** or **Input constant**) must be numbers between 0 and 1: they are the values of α for which the quantiles q_α are required.

The first activity illustrates the use of MINITAB to find quantiles for a continuous random variable.

Computer Activity 13.1   *Quantiles for an exponential distribution* ____

In Computer Activity 12.6, an exponential distribution with mean 437 was used to model the waiting time in days between successive serious earthquakes worldwide. In this activity you will use MINITAB to find the median, quartiles and deciles of this distribution.

(a) Follow the instructions below to find the median.

    ◇   Obtain the **Exponential Distribution** dialogue box.

    ◇   Select **Inverse cumulative probability**.

    ◇   Enter 437 in the **Scale** field (and 0 in the **Threshold** field).

    ◇   To find the median waiting time between serious earthquakes, select **Input constant** and enter 0.5 in the **Input constant** field.

    ◇   Click on **OK** and you will obtain the following output in the Session window.

> **Inverse Cumulative Distribution Function**
>
> Exponential with mean = 437
>
> P(X <= x)   x
>   0.5   302.905

Calc > Probability Distributions > Exponential...

Recall that the median m is $q_{0.5}$.

This says that $P(X \le 302.905) = 0.5$, that is $F(302.905) = 0.5$, so the median waiting time between serious earthquakes is approximately 303 days (as you found in Section 4 of *Unit A5*).

Now find the lower quartile q_L and the upper quartile q_U of the waiting time between serious earthquakes, and hence find the interquartile range of the waiting time between serious earthquakes.

(b) The simplest way to find all the deciles (that is, $q_{0.1}, q_{0.2}, \ldots, q_{0.9}$) is to enter the values $0.1, 0.2, \ldots, 0.9$ in a column of the worksheet, and then type the column name in the **Input column** field in the **Exponential Distribution** dialogue box.

First open a new blank worksheet, then enter the numbers 0.1, 0.2, ..., 0.9 in column C1. Use **Exponential...** to store the deciles $q_{0.1}, q_{0.2}, \ldots, q_{0.9}$ in column C2.

(c) In part (b), you found that $q_{0.2}$ is approximately 98 and $q_{0.6}$ is approximately 400. So, according to the model, approximately 20% of intervals between serious earthquakes are shorter than 98 days, and approximately 40% of intervals exceed 400 days. Interpret the deciles $q_{0.1}$ and $q_{0.8}$.

The next three activities illustrate the use of MINITAB to find quantiles for discrete random variables. Recall from Subsection 4.2 of *Unit A5* that quantiles of a discrete random variable X are values in the range of X. So, for instance, if X takes integer values, then quantiles must be integers.

Computer Activity 13.2   *Quantiles for a binomial distribution* _____

In Computer Activities 8.1 to 8.3, you used MINITAB to find various probabilities associated with a multiple choice examination consisting of twenty questions. Each question had five options, exactly one of which was correct. If X is a random variable representing the number of questions answered correctly by a student who guesses answers at random, then X has a binomial distribution: $X \sim B(20, 0.2)$. In this activity, you will find several quantiles for this distribution.

(a) Use a procedure similar to that used for the median of an exponential distribution in Computer Activity 13.1 to find the median score of students who guess answers at random. You should obtain the following output in the Session window.

Inverse Cumulative Distribution Function

```
Binomial with n = 20 and p = 0.2

x      P(X <= x)         x       P(X <= x)

3      0.411449          4       0.629648
```

Obtain the **Binomial Distribution** dialogue box and enter 20 and 0.2 for the parameters of the distribution.

Values of the cumulative distribution function are given for two consecutive values of x in the range of X. For the first of these, the value of the c.d.f. is less than 0.5: $P(X \le 3) = 0.411449$. For the second, the c.d.f. takes a value greater than 0.5: $P(X \le 4) = 0.629648$. The median m is defined to be the smallest value of x in the range of X for which $F(x) \ge 0.5$. So the median score of students who guess answers at random is the second of the two displayed values of x; that is, the median score is 4.

Find the lower quartile and the upper quartile of X.

(b) The pass mark is to be set so that only one in a thousand students who guess answers at random will pass. What quantile of X should you find in order to determine what the pass mark should be? What should the pass mark be?

Computer Activity 13.3   *More on quantiles of discrete distributions* ⎯

For some discrete random variables and for some values of α, there is a value x in the range of the random variable for which $F(x) = P(X \le x) = \alpha$. When this happens, one of the two probabilities displayed when using **Inverse cumulative probability** will be equal to α.

In this case, the quantile q_α is the value of x corresponding to this probability. To see this for yourself, use MINITAB to find the medians of the following distributions.

(a) A binomial distribution with parameters $n = 5$ and $p = 0.5$.

(b) A discrete uniform distribution on the integers $1, 2, \ldots, 8$.

Use **Integer...** from the **Probability Distributions** submenu of **Calc**.

The method for finding quantiles using MINITAB is essentially the same for all discrete distributions. In the final activity in this chapter, you are asked to find several quantiles for Poisson distributions.

Computer Activity 13.4   *Quantiles for Poisson distributions* ⎯⎯⎯⎯

(a) In Computer Activity 12.6, a Poisson distribution with parameter 3.342 was used to model the number of serious earthquakes that occur in a typical four-year period. According to this model, what is the median number of serious earthquakes that occur in a four-year period?

(b) Telephone calls arrive at a switchboard at random at an average rate of 40 per hour. The number of calls that arrive in an hour may be modelled by a Poisson distribution with parameter 40.

(i) What is the largest number of calls received during any of the 10% of hours that are the quietest?

(ii) What is the largest number of calls received during any of the 1% of hours that are the quietest?

Summary of Chapter 13

In this chapter, you have used MINITAB to calculate quantiles for both continuous and discrete distributions. For a discrete random variable, MINITAB outputs probabilities for two consecutive values in the range of the random variable. The definition of a quantile of a discrete distribution must be used to decide which of these two values is the required quantile.

Chapter 14
Exponential probability plots

In *Unit A5*, you have seen how to construct a probability plot to check whether an exponential distribution is a plausible model for the variation in a data set. In this chapter, you will use MINITAB to obtain exponential probability plots for several data sets, including two that you investigated in Chapter 12. The first data set consists of the intervals between serious earthquakes and the second contains the waiting times between coal-mining explosions.

You explored these two data sets in Computer Activities 12.2 and 12.3.

There are several different ways of deciding which quantiles to use when constructing a probability plot. MINITAB offers four methods. The method described in *Unit A5* is not the one MINITAB produces as a default, so you will need to change the option settings.

Computer Activity 14.1   *Changing the option settings* _____

◇   Choose **Options...** from the **Tools** menu to open the **Options - General** dialogue box.

◇   Click on the + to the left of **Individual Graphs** to display a list of graphs.

◇   Click on **Probability Plots** to view the options available for probability plots.

◇   Under **Y-Scale Type**, select **Score**.

◇   Under **Graph Orientation**, make sure that **Show raw data on horizontal scale** is selected.

◇   Next, you must specify the method to be used to obtain the plot points. The method described in *Unit A5* is obtained by selecting **Mean Rank (Herd-Johnson)**. Click on this to select it.

◇   Click on **OK** to close the dialogue box.

The settings you have selected will be used for all probability plots that you produce unless you change them. Some of the settings can be changed when you produce an individual probability plot. However, the method for calculating the plot points can only be changed using **Options...** from the **Tools** menu.

Computer Activity 14.2   *Intervals between serious earthquakes* _____

The data on serious earthquakes are in the worksheet **earthquakes.mtw**. Open this worksheet now.

Probability plots are obtained using **Probability Plot...** from the **Graph** menu. Obtain an exponential probability plot for the intervals between serious earthquakes, as follows.

◇   Choose **Probability Plot...** from the **Graph** menu. The **Probability Plots** dialogue box will open.

◇   Select **Single** and click on **OK**. The **Probability Plot - Single** dialogue box will open.

◇   The data are in column C1 `interval`, so enter `interval` in the **Graph Variables** field.

◇   Click on the **Distribution...** button to open the **Probability Plot - Distribution** dialogue box.

◇   Click on the down arrow in the **Distribution** field of the **Distribution** panel to view a list of the distributions for which MINITAB will produce a probability plot.

◇   Select `Exponential` from this list.

◇   Leave the **Mean** field under **Historical Parameters** blank.

When displaying a probability plot, by default MINITAB includes 'confidence intervals' on the plot. These are not required here. (They will be explained later in M248.)

◇   Click on the **Data Display** tab to bring the **Data Display** panel uppermost.

◇   Click on **Show confidence interval** to deselect it.

◇   Click on **OK** to close the **Probability Plot - Distribution** dialogue box.

◇   Click on **OK** in the **Probability Plot - Single** dialogue box and the plot shown in Figure 14.1 will be displayed.

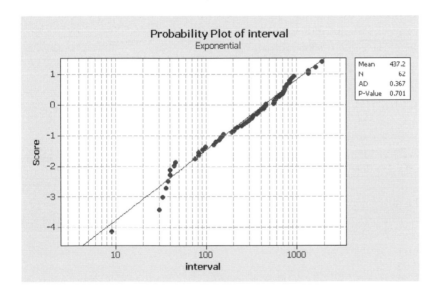

Figure 14.1   An exponential probability plot for the intervals between serious earthquakes

First, notice that the mean waiting time is given to the right of the plot — this is 437.2 days — together with the number of observations (62). Also given is a quantity AD, which is the Anderson–Darling goodness-of-fit test statistic (and its associated p value); this will not be discussed in M248.

Secondly, notice that MINITAB includes a straight line on the plot. If the exponential distribution with mean 437.2 was a perfect fit for these data, then the points would lie on this line. Since the points lie fairly close to this line, an exponential model appears to fit the data quite well.

Finally, observe that this plot does not look the same as the one in *Unit A5*. However, the method used is equivalent to that described in *Unit A5*. Essentially, the difference between this plot and the one given in *Unit A5* is that both variables plotted in Figure 5.1 of *Unit A5* have been transformed in the MINITAB plot using natural logarithms. MINITAB does this by transforming the scale against which the data values $x_{(i)}$ are plotted, and by transforming the quantiles y_i by taking logarithms and plotting $\log y_i$ against a linear scale. MINITAB calls $\log y_i$ the `Score`. In general, if an exponential distribution is a good model for the data, then the plotted points should lie roughly in a straight line *and* the points should be close to the line drawn on the MINITAB plot.

Computer Activity 14.3   Waiting times between major coal-mining explosions

The data on major coal-mining explosions are in the worksheet **coal.mtw**. Open this worksheet now.

A problem arises for this data set when you try to obtain an exponential probability plot. Try this now to see what happens.

When you click on **OK** in the **Probability Plot - Distribution** dialogue box, instead of producing a plot, MINITAB displays an error message in the Session window. This message is displayed because MINITAB will only produce an exponential probability plot if all the data values are positive; and there is a 0 in row 80 of the worksheet. How can this problem be overcome?

Choose **Probability Plot...** from the **Graph** menu and proceed as in Computer Activity 14.2.

If the 0 were to be removed from the worksheet, then MINITAB would produce a plot. However, it would be misleading to simply omit one of the values from the analysis. A value recorded as 0 reflects a very short waiting time between explosions, so a better approach is to replace the 0 with an appropriate small value.

The data are waiting times in days between successive major coal-mining explosions, and the 0 occurred because there were two explosions on 6 December 1875. Assuming the explosions did not occur simultaneously, then the waiting time was non-zero but less than one day. Whatever value in this range you choose, the resulting exponential probability plot will look almost exactly the same, so the precise value you choose to replace the 0 does not matter. (You might like to verify this for yourself.)

Replace the 0 in row 80 by a suitable small value and obtain an exponential probability plot. What can you deduce from this plot?

Computer Activity 14.4   Memory recall times ──────────────

In a study of memory recall times, a series of stimulus words was shown to a subject on a computer screen. For each word, the subject was asked to recall either a pleasant or an unpleasant memory associated with that word. Successful recall of a memory was indicated by the subject pressing a bar on the computer keyboard. The recall times (in seconds) were collected for twenty pleasant and twenty unpleasant memories: these data are stored in the worksheet **memory.mtw**. Open this worksheet now.

The recall times for pleasant memories are in column `C1` of the worksheet (labelled `pleasant`) and those for unpleasant memories are in column `C2` (labelled `unpleasant`). Obtain two exponential probability plots, one for each set of recall times. Is an exponential distribution a plausible model for either set of recall times?

Summary of Chapter 14

In this chapter, you have used MINITAB to obtain exponential probability plots for several data sets, two of which you explored in Chapter 12. You obtained the plots using **Probability Plot...** from the **Graph** menu.

Computer Exercises on Block A

Computer Exercise 1   *Strength of Kraft paper*

The tensile strength of Kraft paper (in pounds per square inch) was measured against the percentage of hardwood in the batch of pulp from which the paper was produced. Nineteen observations were recorded. The data are in the worksheet **paper.mtw**. The tensile strength and the percentage of hardwood in each batch of pulp are in columns labelled **strength** and **hardwood**, respectively.

Joglekar, G., Schuenemeyer, J.H. and LaRiccia, V. (1989) Lack-of-fit testing when replicates are not available. *American Statistician*, **43**, 135–143.

(a) Produce a scatterplot of the data with tensile strength on the vertical axis. Label the axes **tensile strength** and **hardwood content**.

(b) Use your scatterplot to comment on the relationship between the two variables. Do there appear to be any outliers?

Computer Exercise 2   *Fasting serum growth hormone*

The levels of fasting serum growth hormone (in nanograms per millilitre) were measured for 63 diabetic patients and for 31 patients in a control group. The data are in the MINITAB worksheet **fsg-hormone.mtw**, in columns labelled **diabetic** and **control**, respectively. There are biological reasons why the level of this hormone might be different in diabetics compared with people who do not have diabetes.

Hansen, A.P. (1973) Abnormal serum growth hormone response to exercise in maturity-onset diabetics. *Diabetes*, **22**, 619–628.

(a) Construct comparative boxplots of the fasting serum growth hormone levels.

(b) Comment on what the boxplots tell you about the level of this hormone in diabetics and in controls. For the purposes of making the comparison between the diabetics and the controls, would it help to transform the data? Give reasons for your answer. If you think the data should be transformed, suggest an appropriate transformation, make it, obtain comparative boxplots for the transformed data, and comment.

Computer Exercise 3   *Passengers on standby*

According to the publicity department of an international airline, on average 10% of people making reservations on their scheduled London–Rome service fail to turn up for their flight. Suppose that, on a particular day, the flight is fully booked for 140 passengers with 16 more waiting on standby.

(a) If the airline's claim is accurate, what is the distribution of X, the number of passengers who do not turn up for the flight?

(b) Find the probability that all the standby passengers get a seat on the flight.

(c) Find the probability that exactly half of the standby passengers get a seat on the flight.

Computer Exercise 4

Suppose that the occurrences of major explosive volcanic eruptions in the northern hemisphere may be adequately modelled by a Poisson process with rate $\lambda = 0.0352$ per month.

This is the model that was proposed in Exercise 3.1 of *Unit A5*.

(a) Find the probability that there will be more than five such eruptions in a ten-year period.

(b) Find the probability that the waiting time between successive eruptions will be less than six months.

(c) Find the value x such that only 5% of intervals between successive eruptions are shorter than x months.

(d) Find the value y such that only 1% of intervals between successive eruptions exceed y years.

Computer Exercise 5   *Admissions to an intensive care unit*

The worksheet **icu40.mtw** contains data on the times between successive admissions to an intensive care unit. The original data give the day and time of admission for each patient. The purpose of collecting the data was to identify any systematic variations in arrival rates. The arrival times were differenced to give the waiting times between admissions (to the nearest half hour). The worksheet contains the first 40 waiting times.

The original data are in the worksheet **icu.mtw**.

(a) Investigate whether or not these data are consistent with an exponential distribution being a good model for the waiting times between admissions.

(b) The data are ordered. Investigate whether the data are consistent with the admission rate remaining constant over time.

Cox, D.R. and Snell, E.J. (1981) *Applied Statistics*. Chapman and Hall, London. (The data were collected by Dr A. Barr, Oxford Regional Hospital Board.)

Solutions to Computer Activities

Solution 1.6

The pie chart required is shown in Figure S.1.

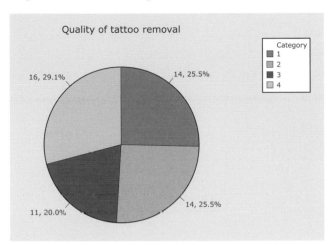

Figure S.1   A pie chart for quality of tattoo removal

The pie chart may be obtained as follows.

◊   Choose **Pie Chart...** from the **Graph** menu.

◊   In the **Pie Chart** dialogue box, check that **Chart counts of unique values** is selected, and enter C5 or score in the **Categorical variables** field.

◊   Click on the **Labels...** button to open the **Pie Chart - Labels** dialogue box.

◊   Type Quality of tattoo removal in the **Title** field of the **Titles/Footnotes** panel.

◊   Click on the **Slice Labels** tab and select **Frequency**, **Percent** and **Draw a line from label to slice**.

◊   Click on **OK** to close this dialogue box, then click on **OK** in the **Pie Chart** dialogue box to obtain the pie chart.

Solution 1.7

The pie chart required is shown in Figure S.2.

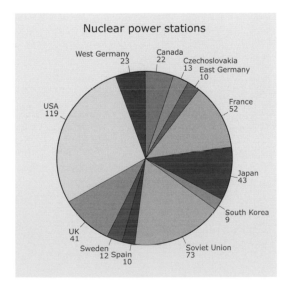

Figure S.2   A pie chart for nuclear power stations

Solution 1.8

In the **Pie Chart** dialogue box, click on **Pie Options...** to open the **Pie Chart - Options** dialogue box. Enter 5 in the field labelled **Combine slices of this percent or less**. Then, when you produce a pie chart, the data will be combined for countries with less than 5% of the total number of power stations. The pie chart that is required is shown in Figure S.3.

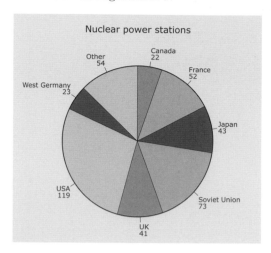

Figure S.3 A pie chart with the smallest groups combined

Alternatively, the pie chart can be obtained by editing the pie chart you obtained in Computer Activity 1.7, as follows.

◇   Select the pie chart, then double-click on it (or press **Ctrl+T**) to open the **Edit Pie** dialogue box.

◇   Click on the **Options** tab to view the **Options** panel.

◇   Enter 5 in the field labelled **Combine slices of this percent or less**.

◇   Click on **OK**.

Solution 2.2

The required bar chart is shown in Figure S.4.

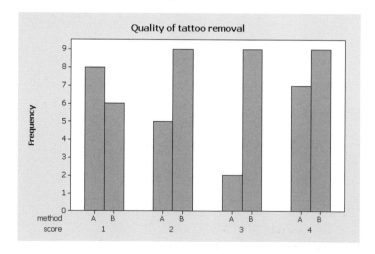

Figure S.4 Quality for different methods of tattoo removal

This was obtained by entering `score method` in the **Categorical variables** field of the **Bar Chart - Counts of unique values, Cluster** dialogue box (and by entering a title and editing the *y*-axis label).

Solution 2.4

The bar chart required is shown in Figure S.5.

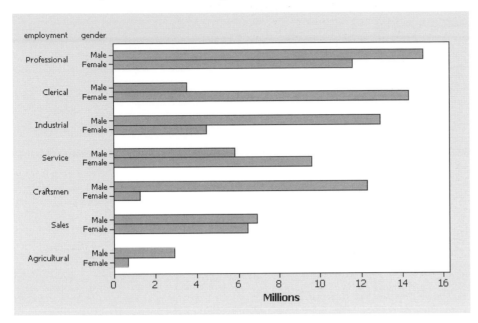

Figure S.5 USA workforce data: 1986 averages

This bar chart was produced using the following settings.

In the **Bar Charts** dialogue box:

◇ `Values from a table` was selected from the **Bars represent** drop-down list;

◇ **Cluster** was selected from the **One column of values** options.

In the **Bar Chart - Values from a table, One column of values, Cluster** dialogue box:

◇ `workforce` was entered in the **Graph variables** field, and `employment gender` in the **Categorical variables for grouping** field.

In the **Bar Chart - Options** dialogue box:

◇ **Decreasing Y** was selected.

In the **Bar Chart - Scale** dialogue box:

◇ **Transpose value and category scales** was selected.

Finally, the default title was deleted (by selecting the title on the bar chart, and pressing the **Delete** key); and the label on the horizontal axis was edited (by selecting it on the bar chart and pressing **Ctrl+T**, then typing `Millions` in the **Text** field of the **Edit Axis Label** dialogue box).

Solution 3.2

Obtain the **Edit Bars** dialogue box, as described in Computer Activity 3.1. In the **Binning** panel, select **Cutpoint** for all three diagrams. To obtain a diagram similar to Figure 3.2 of *Unit A1*, enter `1:4/0.3` in the **Midpoint/Cutpoint positions** field. The corresponding entries required to obtain diagrams similar to Figures 3.3(a) and 3.3(b) are `0.8:3.8/0.3` and `0.9:3.9/0.3`, respectively.

Solution 3.3

(a) The histogram in Figure S.6 was obtained by selecting **Cutpoint** in the **Binning** panel of the **Edit Bars** dialogue box and entering 100:160/5 in the **Midpoint/Cutpoint positions** field.

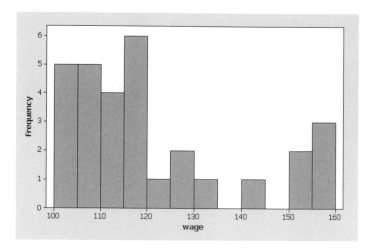

Figure S.6 A histogram for wages of production line workers

(b) The histogram suggests that the production line workers are split into at least two identifiable groups on the basis of their wages. The main group is towards the lower end of the wage range, while there appears to be a second smaller group at the top end of the wage range.

Solution 3.5

The scatterplot required is shown in Figure S.7.

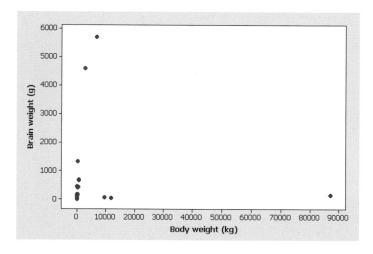

Figure S.7 Body weights and brain weights of animals

Solution 4.1

The output obtained for the mothers with six years or less of education is shown below.

Variable	N	N*	Mean	SE Mean	StDev	Minimum	Q1	Median	Q3
short	19	0	8.16	1.19	5.19	0.00	3.00	10.00	13.00

Variable	Maximum
short	14.00

The mean and standard deviation are 8.16 and 5.19, respectively. The range is $14 - 0 = 14$; and the interquartile range is $13 - 3 = 10$. These values agree with the results obtained in Exercise 4.1 of *Unit A1*.

Solution 4.2

The value given by MINITAB is −0.327483, so to two decimal places the sample skewness is equal to −0.33. This is the value given in Subsection 4.3 of *Unit A1*.

Solution 4.3

(a) The histogram of the birth weights of the infants who survived has a longer right tail than left tail, so the data seem to be right-skew, but not markedly so. This is confirmed by the sample skewness, which is 0.250587, or approximately 0.25.

(b) The histogram of the birth weights of the infants who died also has a longer right tail than left tail, and the data seem to be more skewed than those for the infants who survived. This is confirmed by the sample skewness, which is 0.530657, or approximately 0.53.

(c) The mean and standard deviation of the birth weights of the infants who survived are 2.307 and 0.665, respectively. The mean and standard deviation of the birth weights of the infants who died are 1.6917 and 0.5176, respectively. So the mean birth weight of the infants who survived is higher than the mean birth weight of those who died by a factor of over a third. The standard deviation is also higher, by a factor of almost 30%.

Solution 5.2

You should obtain a boxplot as shown in Figure S.8.

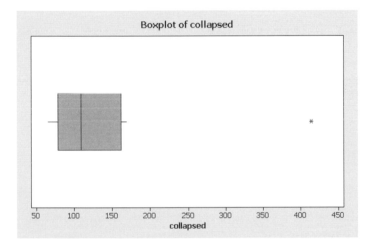

Figure S.8　A horizontal MINITAB boxplot for the data on collapsed runners

This time the boxplot is drawn horizontally and looks more like that in Figure 1.1 of *Unit A2*. You may (or may not!) agree that, in this case, a horizontal boxplot is preferable. There are two reasons for this view. First, a horizontal boxplot spreads out the values more; and secondly, with only a single boxplot the result is aesthetically more pleasing. However, where several boxplots are drawn on the same graph, they sometimes look better if they are displayed vertically.

Solution 5.3

The boxplot required is shown in Figure S.9 (overleaf).

It was obtained by entering **percentage** in the **Graph variables** field in the **Boxplot - One Y, Simple** dialogue box and selecting **Transpose value and category scales** in the **Boxplot - Scale** dialogue box. The axis label was then edited.

Unless you have stopped and restarted MINITAB since doing the previous computer activity, the option **Transpose value and category scales** should still be checked.

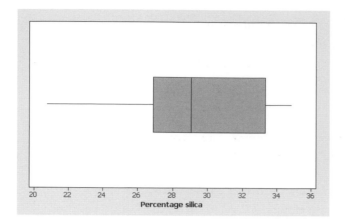

The default title has been omitted from Figure S.9.

Figure S.9   A boxplot for the silica data

Solution 5.5

The comparative boxplots produced by MINITAB are shown in Figure S.10. They are indeed similar to those in Figure 1.7 of *Unit A2*.

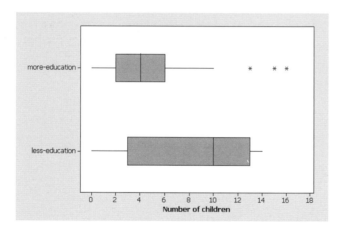

Figure S.10   Boxplots of family size

Solution 5.6

In the worksheet, the BSA measurements for the three groups of mice are stored in separate columns (called `placebo`, `ADplacebo` and `ADinsulin`). In order to produce comparative boxplots in MINITAB, in the **Boxplots** dialogue box, **Simple** must be selected under **Multiple Y's**.

In the **Boxplot - Multiple Y's, Simple** dialogue box, `ADinsulin` must be entered first in the **Graph variables** field, followed by `ADplacebo` and `placebo`. After deleting the title and editing the labels as specified, the comparative boxplots are as shown in Figure S.11.

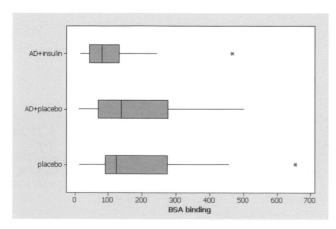

Figure S.11   Boxplots of the (untransformed) BSA data

Solution 5.7

The steps required to transform the BSA binding data are given below.

◇ Choose **Calculator...** from the **Calc** menu.

◇ To create a column called `log(BSA)` to contain the transformed data, type `log(BSA)` in the **Store result in variable** field.

Now enter an expression for the logarithm (base *e*) of the BSA values in the **Expression** field, as follows.

◇ Scroll through the list of functions until you find `Natural log (log base e)`, click on it, and then press **Select** to insert `LN(number)` in the **Expression** field.

◇ The word `number` is highlighted. Double-click on `BSA` in the list of variables on the left of the dialogue box to replace `number` with `BSA`.

◇ Click on **OK**.

An alternative is to type `LN(BSA)` directly in the **Expression** field.

A new column called `log(BSA)` will appear in your worksheet; this will contain the logarithms of the values in the BSA column. (Note that, because all the BSA values have been stacked in one column, you only have to apply the log transformation once to this stacked column, rather than doing it separately for each of the three original columns of data.)

Boxplots of the transformed data are shown in Figure S.12. They are arguably more helpful for comparison purposes than those in Figure S.11, which you produced in Computer Activity 5.6.

Select **With Groups** under **One Y** in the **Boxplots** dialogue box (as described in Computer Activity 5.4).

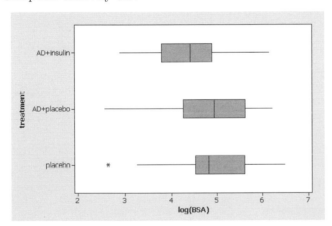

Figure S.12 Boxplots of the log transformed BSA data

Solution 5.8

The boxplots are shown in Figure S.13.

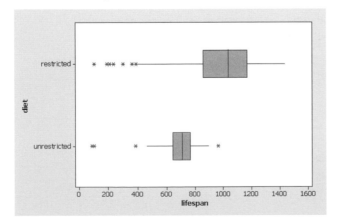

Figure S.13 Boxplots of the (untransformed) lifespans of rats

It is fairly clear from these boxplots that the lifespans of the rats on the restricted diet are more spread out and, in terms of location, generally greater than the lifespans of the rats on unrestricted diets. Also, the smaller values tend to be more spread out than the larger ones — that is, the data appear to be left-skew.

Solution 5.9

Arguably there is no particular need to transform the data, since the pattern of the data is reasonably clear. However, you were asked to carry out a square transformation and see what happened! The resulting boxplots are shown in Figure S.14.

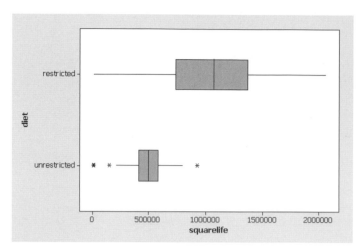

Figure S.14   Boxplots of the squares of the lifetimes of rats

The transformation has removed the skewness that was evident in the original data; but arguably, in terms of comparison between the groups, the picture is no clearer than before. The message here is that, even when data sets are skew, it is not always necessary to transform the data to make a clear comparison using boxplots.

Solution 5.10

(a)   The boxplots required are shown in Figure S.15.

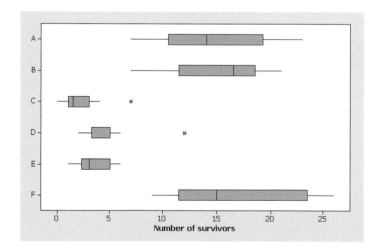

Figure S.15   Boxplots of insects surviving different insecticides

It is plain from this diagram that many more insects tended to survive with insecticides A, B and F than with C, D and E. Also, the number of survivors per batch was more variable for insecticides A, B and F than for the other insecticides.

(b) There is no compelling reason for trying a transformation. There is no obviously awkward skewness, at least not in any consistent direction. The groups with the largest means are more spread out than the others, and a transformation that removed right skewness would tend to reduce that effect. However, on the whole, the data are best left as they are. It is just as important to realize when to leave well alone as it is to recognize the need for a transformation.

Solution 6.1

Choose **Bar Chart. . .** from the **Graph** menu. Select **Values from a table** from the **Bars represent** drop-down list, select **Simple** under **One column of values**, and click on **OK**. In the dialogue box that opens, enter `musculoskeletal` in the **Graph variables** field and `group` in the **Categorical variable** field. A bar chart with horizontal bars is shown in Figure S.16.

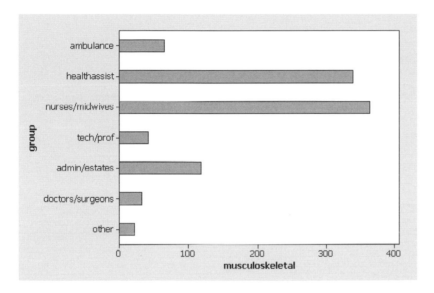

The value and category scales were transposed to obtain this bar chart.

Figure S.16   A bar chart of retirements for musculoskeletal reasons

Solution 8.2

(a) The probability required is

$$P(T < 4) = P(T \le 3) = F(3).$$

Using **Cumulative probability** and setting **Input constant** equal to 3 gives $0.411449 \simeq 0.4114$.

(b) The probability required is

$$
\begin{aligned}
P(4 \le T \le 9) &= P(T \le 9) - P(T < 4) \\
&= P(T \le 9) - P(T \le 3) \\
&= F(9) - F(3) \\
&= 0.997405 - 0.411449 \\
&= 0.585956 \\
&\simeq 0.5860.
\end{aligned}
$$

Solution 8.4

(a) If X is the number of questions out of 10 that are answered correctly, then $X \sim B(10, 0.125)$. So you need to set **Number of trials** equal to 10 and **Event probability** equal to 0.125.

The probability that a student just passes is $P(X = 5)$. Using **Probability** and setting **Input constant** equal to 5 gives

$$P(X = 5) = 0.0039445.$$

So the probability that a student who guesses answers at random just passes the test is approximately 0.0039.

The probability that a student fails is $P(X \leq 4)$. Using **Cumulative probability** and setting **Input constant** equal to 4 gives

$$P(X \leq 4) = 0.995545.$$

So the probability that a student who guesses answers at random fails the test is approximately 0.9955.

(b) If X is the number of questions out of 30 that are answered correctly in this test, then $X \sim B(30, 0.25)$. So you need to set **Number of trials** equal to 30 and **Event probability** equal to 0.25.

The probability that a student who guesses answers at random passes the test is

$$P(X \geq 15) = 1 - P(X \leq 14).$$

Using **Cumulative probability** and setting **Input constant** equal to 14 gives

$$P(X \leq 14) = 0.997250.$$

So the probability that a student who guesses answers at random passes the test is

$$P(X \geq 15) = 1 - 0.997250 = 0.002750 \simeq 0.0028.$$

Solution 8.5

If X is the number of defective fuses in a bag, then $X \sim B(8, 0.012)$. You need to set **Number of trials** equal to 8 and **Event probability** equal to 0.012.

(a) The probability required is $P(X = 1)$.

Using **Probability** and setting **Input constant** equal to 1 gives 0.0882206. So the probability that a bag contains exactly one defective fuse is approximately 0.0882.

(b) The probability required is

$$P(X < 3) = P(X \leq 2) = F(2).$$

Using **Cumulative probability** and setting **Input constant** equal to 2 gives 0.999908. So the probability that a bag contains fewer than 3 defective fuses is approximately 0.9999.

Solution 9.1

(a) When I generated samples as specified, the histogram for the sample of size 50 was the most jagged of the three, then that for the sample of size 500. The heights of the bars on the histogram for the sample of size 5000 were very similar. The relative frequencies of the months seemed to be settling down as the sample size increased.

(b) For samples of size 82, several of the histograms I obtained were as jagged as the histogram of the data. It is possible that the variation in the numbers of deaths occurring in different months is just due to chance. It seems plausible that deaths are as likely to occur in any particular month as in any other. A discrete uniform distribution appears to be a reasonable model here.

Solution 9.2

I used the program to take quite a large number of samples of size 254 from the uniform distribution $U(0, 24)$. In general, their histograms were less jagged than the histogram of the data: none of the histograms had peaks as high or troughs as low as those in the histogram of the data. So the continuous uniform distribution does not appear to fit the data very well: this suggests that admissions are more likely to occur at some times of the day than at others.

Solution 9.3

There are 16 small squares in each larger square. If each small square is coloured black with probability 0.29, independently of the other squares, then the number of black small squares in a larger square has a binomial distribution with parameters $n = 16$ and $p = 0.29$.

Solution 9.4

(a) The histogram that I obtained of the screen data was very similar in shape to the diagram of the probability function of the binomial distribution $B(16, 0.29)$. The histograms of the samples from the binomial model were very similar in shape to the histogram of the screen data. It looks as though the binomial model is a good fit for the data. There is no reason to doubt that the colouring algorithm is operating successfully.

(b) I obtained similar results and drew similar conclusions for the other values of p that I used.

Solution 9.5

For each of the (unknown) values of p that I used, the histogram of the data from the screen was very similar in shape to the probability function of the binomial distribution $B(16, p)$, where p was estimated from the data. The histograms of the samples from the binomial model were very similar in shape to the histogram of the screen data. It looks as though the binomial model is a good fit for the data. There is no reason to doubt that the colouring algorithm is operating successfully.

Solution 9.6

(a) The histograms I obtained were all very similar in shape and with a similar amount of jaggedness to the histogram of the data. It looks as though the normal model fits the data quite well.

(b) I fitted a normal model with parameters $\mu = 160$ and $\sigma = 6$. The sample size is much smaller than that in part (a), so histograms of samples are much more jagged than those I obtained in part (a). What is important here is whether the amount of jaggedness is similar for the data and the samples: this was the case for the samples I obtained. Again, it looks as though a normal model fits the data quite well.

You may have used slightly different parameter values; for example, 159.8 and 6.03. That is all right.

(c) This time I fitted a normal model with parameters $\mu = 315$ and $\sigma = 131$. The sample size is only 55 and the histogram of the data is very jagged. The histograms for the samples I obtained were just as jagged.

All real values, negative and positive, are possible for a normally distributed random variable; and several of the samples I obtained contained one or two negative values. But nicotine levels cannot be negative. So it looks as though a normal model does not fit the data well in this case. However, remember that the normal distribution is only a model — it is not an exact representation of the distribution of nicotine levels among smokers. It may well be usable for practical purposes, and this is all that is required of a model.

(d) In each case, I fitted a normal model with parameters μ and σ similar to the sample mean and sample standard deviation. Histograms of samples from the normal model were as jagged as the histogram of the data: it looks as though a normal model fits the data quite well.

Solution 12.1

A column containing the numbers 1, 2, ..., 62, which is required in part (b), can be created as follows.

◇ Choose **Simple Set of Numbers...** from the **Make Patterned Data** submenu of **Calc** to obtain the **Simple Set of Numbers** dialogue box.

◇ To store the numbers in a column called `number`, type `number` in the **Store patterned data in** field.

◇ All the integers from 1 to 62 are required, so enter `1` in the **From first value** field and `62` in the **To last value** field.

The other fields should each contain default values of `1`. (If by any chance they do not, then change the values in these fields to `1`.)

◇ Click on **OK**.

The numbers 1 to 62 will be stored in column `C3` (the first available column in the worksheet).

Solution 12.2

(a) The mean and standard deviation can be found as follows.

◇ Obtain the **Display Descriptive Statistics** dialogue box.

◇ Enter `C1` or `interval` in the **Variables** field and click on **OK**.

Stat > Basic Statistics > Display Descriptive Statistics...

The MINITAB output includes the values of the mean and standard deviation. The values given are 437.2 and 399.9, respectively. As observed in *Unit A5*, these values are reasonably close, as you would expect them to be if the data are observations from an exponential distribution.

Recall that the mean and standard deviation of an exponential distribution are equal.

Alternatively, you can find the mean and standard deviation using **Store Descriptive Statistics...**. In this case, the values given by MINITAB are 437.210 and 399.927, respectively.

(b) The histogram required is shown in Figure S.17.

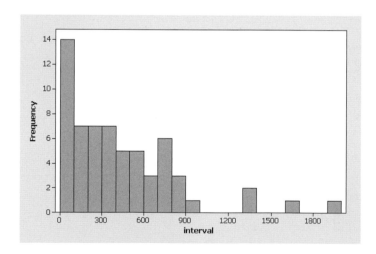

Figure S.17   A histogram of the waiting times

This histogram can be obtained as follows.

◇ Choose **Histogram...** from the **Graph** menu.

◇ Select **Simple** and click on **OK** to obtain the **Histogram - Simple** dialogue box.

◇ Enter `interval` in the **Graph variables** field.

◇ Click on **OK**.

The scale on the horizontal axis can be edited as follows.

◇ Select the scale and press **Ctrl+T** to open the **Edit Scale** dialogue box.

◇ Click on the **Binning** tab so that the **Binning** panel is uppermost.

◇ Select **Cutpoint** under **Interval Type**.

◇ Select **Midpoint/Cutpoint positions** and enter 0:2000/100 in its field.

◇ Click on **OK** and the groupings will change.

As observed in *Unit A5*, the highest frequencies are for the shortest intervals. The frequencies tend to tail off for higher waiting times. This general shape is consistent with the data being observations from an exponential distribution.

Solution 12.3

(a) MINITAB gives the values 213.4 and 313.5 for the sample mean and sample standard deviation. A histogram of the data is shown in Figure S.18.

The scale was edited to produce this histogram by selecting **Cutpoint** under **Interval Type** in the **Binning** panel of the **Edit Scale** dialogue box and entering 0:2400/100 in the **Midpoint/Cutpoint positions** field.

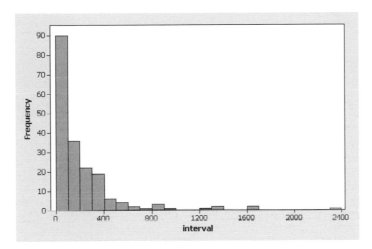

Figure S.18   Intervals between coal-mining explosions

The histogram is highly skewed with a peak for low values, as expected for data from an exponential distribution. However, although the mean and standard deviation are of the same order, their values are not very close. There is some doubt about whether the waiting times between explosions are exponentially distributed.

(b) A scatterplot showing the number of explosions that have occurred against time is shown in Figure S.19.

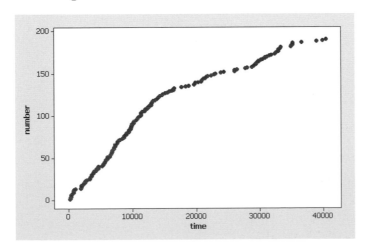

Figure S.19   A scatterplot of explosions against time

It looks as though the rate of occurrence of coal-mining explosions decreased during the period of observation. Explosions were less frequent towards the end of the period.

(c) The rate of occurrence of coal-mining explosions does not appear to have
     remained constant over the period of observation. So a Poisson process is not
     a suitable model for the occurrences of coal-mining explosions. There is also
     some doubt about whether an exponential distribution is a good model for
     the waiting times between explosions.

Solution 12.4

The scatterplot is shown in Figure S.20.

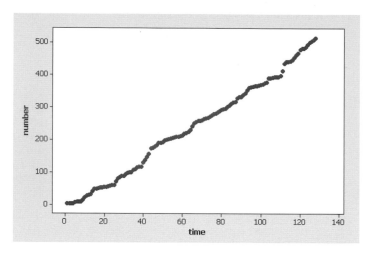

Figure S.20   Computer breakdowns

The points lie roughly along a straight line, so the rate of occurrence of
breakdowns appears to have remained constant over the period of observation.

Solution 12.5

(a) MINITAB gives the values 4.016 and 3.808 for the mean and standard
     deviation. So the sample variance is 3.808^2 or approximately 14.5. The mean
     and variance of a Poisson distribution are equal. However, the values of the
     sample mean and sample variance are not close. These results suggest that a
     Poisson distribution is unlikely to be a good model for the number of
     breakdowns occurring in a week.

(b) The histogram is shown in Figure S.21.

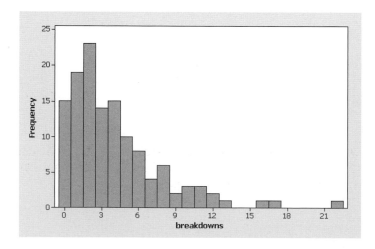

Figure S.21   A histogram of the breakdowns data

Note that you were asked to obtain a histogram rather than a bar chart for the following reason. When using **Bar Chart...**, the values in `breakdowns` are treated as categories, so when a bar chart is produced, only values that occur at least once are plotted on the horizontal axis. This means that, for example, there are no bars for 14 or 15 breakdowns, and the bars for 13 and 16 are adjacent. Hence a bar chart gives a misleading impression of the shape of the distribution of the data. You can see this for yourself if you obtain a bar chart of the data. To obtain a bar chart with gaps for missing values on the horizontal axis, the data must be entered in the worksheet with the values $0, 1, \ldots, 22$ in one column and frequencies (some of which will be 0) in a second column. The bar chart can then be obtained by choosing `Values from a table` from the **Bars represent** drop-down list in the **Bar Charts** dialogue box. (If you want to try this, then you can obtain the frequencies using **Tally Individual Variables...** from the **Tables** submenu of the **Stat** menu.)

(c) The diagram required is shown in Figure S.22.

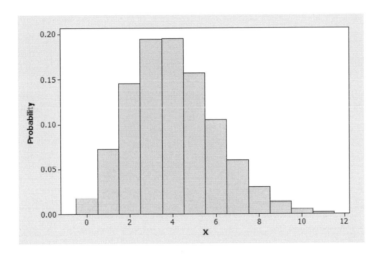

Figure S.22 The probability mass function of a Poisson(4.016) distribution

Although both diagrams are right-skew, the histogram of the data is more strongly skewed than the probability mass function: its peak is further to the left than the peak of the p.m.f. The Poisson distribution with mean 4.016 is not a good model for the number of failures in a week. So a Poisson process is unlikely to be a good model for the occurrences of breakdowns of the computer.

Solution 12.6

(a) If X is a random variable representing the number of serious earthquakes that occur in a typical four-year period, then X has a Poisson distribution with parameter

$$\lambda t = \frac{62}{27107} \times 1461 \simeq 3.342.$$

Allowing for a leap year, there are 1461 days in a four-year period.

(b) Obtain the **Poisson Distribution** dialogue box. Enter the value `3.342` in the **Mean** field. You need to select **Probability** for the first probability and **Cumulative probability** for the other two. In each case, you must enter an appropriate value in the **Input constant** field.

Calc > Probability Distributions > Poisson...

(i) The probability required is

$$P(X = 5) = 0.122868 \simeq 0.1229.$$

(ii) The probability required is

$$P(X < 3) = P(X \leq 2) = F(2) = 0.351061 \simeq 0.3511.$$

(iii) The probability required is

$$P(X \geq 8) = 1 - P(X \leq 7)$$
$$= 1 - F(7)$$
$$= 1 - 0.978882$$
$$= 0.021118 \simeq 0.0211.$$

The values above are those given by MINITAB.

(c) If T is a random variable representing the waiting time between successive serious earthquakes, then T has an exponential distribution with parameter $\lambda = 62/27107$.

The mean waiting time in days is $1/\lambda = 437$ (to the nearest day).

(d) Obtain the **Exponential Distribution** dialogue box. Enter 437 in the **Scale** field and 0 in the **Threshold** field of the **Exponential Distribution** dialogue box. You need to select **Cumulative probability** for both calculations.

Calc > Probability Distributions > Exponential...

(i) The probability required is

$$P(T < 30) = F(30) = 0.0663465 \simeq 0.066.$$

Remember that T is a continuous random variable, so $P(T < 30) = P(T \leq 30) = F(30)$.

(ii) Assuming neither year is a leap year, there are 730 days in a two-year period, so the probability required is

$$P(T > 730) = 1 - P(T \leq 730)$$
$$= 1 - F(730)$$
$$= 1 - 0.811843$$
$$\simeq 0.188.$$

Solution 12.7

(a) If X is a random variable representing the number of alpha particles emitted in a one-minute period, then X has a Poisson distribution with parameter

$$\lambda t = 0.517 \times 60 = 31.02.$$

(b) Obtain the **Poisson Distribution** dialogue box. Enter 31.02 in the **Mean** field. Select **Probability** for the first probability and **Cumulative probability** for the other two. In each case you must enter an appropriate value in the **Input constant** field.

(i) The probability required is

$$P(X = 30) = 0.0714133 \simeq 0.0714.$$

(ii) The probability required is

$$P(X < 20) = P(X \leq 19) = F(19) = 0.0142899 \simeq 0.0143.$$

(iii) The probability required is

$$P(X \geq 50) = 1 - P(X \leq 49)$$
$$= 1 - F(49)$$
$$= 1 - 0.998959$$
$$\simeq 0.0010.$$

(c) If T is a random variable representing the intervals between successive emissions, then T has an exponential distribution with parameter $\lambda = 0.517$.

(d) Obtain the **Exponential Distribution** dialogue box. Since $\lambda = 0.517$, the mean of the distribution is $1/\lambda \simeq 1.934$, so enter **1.934** in the **Scale** field (and **0** in the **Threshold** field). You need to select **Cumulative probability** for both calculations.

(i) The probability required is

$$P(T < 0.5) = F(0.5) = 0.227815 \simeq 0.2278.$$

(ii) The probability required is

$$P(T > 3) = 1 - F(3) = 1 - 0.788004 \simeq 0.2120.$$

Solution 13.1

(a) Since $q_L = q_{0.25}$, enter **0.25** in the **Input constant** field.

The MINITAB output states that $P(X \leq 125.717) = 0.25$, so the lower quartile is approximately 126 days.

Similarly, $q_U = q_{0.75}$, so input the value **0.75**. From the MINITAB output, the upper quartile is approximately 606 days.

Hence the interquartile range is approximately $606 - 126 = 480$ days.

(b) Either type the values **0.1, 0.2, ..., 0.9** directly in column C1 of the worksheet, or use **Make Patterned Data** from the **Calc** menu as follows. Using **Simple Set of Numbers...**, enter C1 in the **Store patterned data in** field, **0.1** in the **From first value** field, **0.9** in the **To last value** field and **0.1** in the **In steps of** field.

When finding the deciles, select **Input column** in the **Exponential Distribution** dialogue box, enter C1 in its field and C2 in the **Optional storage** field. The deciles, rounded to the nearest integer, are listed in the table below.

α	0.1	0.2	0.3	0.4	0.5	0.6	0.7	0.8	0.9
q_α	46	98	156	223	303	400	526	703	1006

(c) Since $q_{0.1} \simeq 46$, approximately 10% of gaps between serious earthquakes are shorter than 46 days.

Since $q_{0.8} \simeq 703$, approximately 80% of gaps between serious earthquakes are shorter than 703 days and therefore approximately 20% exceed 703 days.

Solution 13.2

(a) If the value **0.25** is entered in the **Input constant** field, then MINITAB displays the following results:

$$P(X \leq 2) = 0.206085, \quad P(X \leq 3) = 0.411449.$$

So the lower quartile q_L is 3.

Similarly, entering the value **0.75** leads to

$$P(X \leq 4) = 0.629648, \quad P(X \leq 5) = 0.804208.$$

So the upper quartile is 5.

(b) At least 999 out of 1000 students who guess must score less than the pass mark, so the pass mark x must be chosen so that $P(X < x) \geq 0.999$, that is, $P(X \leq x - 1) \geq 0.999$. So find $q_{0.999}$; this will give the highest score that will be a fail.

For a discrete random variable, $P(X < x) = P(X \leq x - 1)$.

According to MINITAB, $P(X \leq 9) = 0.997405$ (which is less than 0.999) and $P(X < 10) = 0.999437$ (which exceeds 0.999). So $q_{0.999}$ is equal to 10.

The pass mark should be 11.

inomial distribution, $B(5, 0.5)$, MINITAB gives the probabilities
$) = 0.1875$ and $P(X \le 2) = 0.5$, so the median is 2.

.iscrete uniform distribution on the integers $1, 2, \ldots, 8$, MINITAB
gives the two probabilities $P(X \le 3) = 0.375$ and $P(X \le 4) = 0.5$. The
median is 4.

Notice that, in both cases, the median is the second of the two values for
which probabilities are given.

Solution 13.4

(a) For a Poisson distribution with mean 3.342, MINITAB gives the two
probabilities

$$P(X \le 2) = 0.351061, \quad P(X \le 3) = 0.571078.$$

So, according to the exponential model, the median number of serious
earthquakes in a four-year period is 3.

(b) (i) For a Poisson distribution with mean 40, when you enter the value `0.1`
in the **Input constant** field, MINITAB gives

$$P(X \le 31) = 0.0855206, \quad P(X \le 32) = 0.115304.$$

So the largest number of calls received during any of the 10% of hours
that are the quietest is 32.

(ii) When you enter `0.01` in the **Input constant** field, you obtain
$P(X \le 25) = 0.0075664$, $P(X \le 26) = 0.0123106$. So even during one of
the 1% of hours that are the quietest, as many as 26 calls may be
received.

Solution 14.3

The probability plot in Figure S.23 was obtained after replacing the 0 in row 80 of
the worksheet by 0.25. (The statistics displayed by MINITAB to the right of the
plot have been deleted as they are not required.)

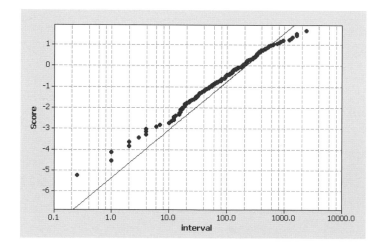

Figure S.23   An exponential probability plot for the waiting times between
explosions

The points do not lie roughly along the straight line. So an exponential model is
not a good one for the intervals between major coal-mining explosions.

Your exploration of these data
in Computer Activity 12.3
suggested that an exponential
model might not be a good one
for these data.

Solution 14.4

The two probability plots are shown in Figure S.24.

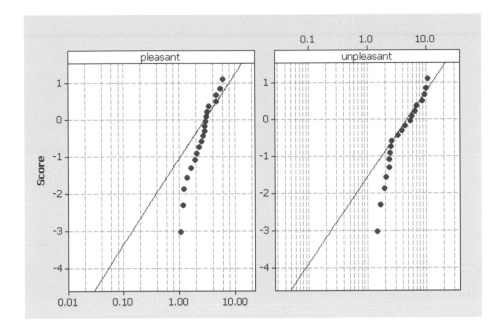

Figure S.24 Exponential probability plots for the recall times of pleasant and unpleasant memories

You probably obtained the probability plots in two separate Graph windows. The plots can be obtained side-by-side in a Graph window, as shown in Figure S.24, as follows.

◇ Obtain the **Probability Plot - Single** dialogue box.

◇ Enter pleasant unpleasant in the **Graph variables** field.

◇ Use the **Probability Plot - Distribution** dialogue box to specify that exponential probability plots without confidence intervals are required.

◇ Click on the **Multiple Graphs...** button to open the **Probability Plot - Multiple Graphs** dialogue box.

◇ Under **Show Graph Variables** in the **Multiple Variables** panel, select **In separate panels of the same graph**.

◇ Click on **OK** to close the dialogue box, then click on **OK** again and the graphs will be produced.

In both plots, the points do not lie roughly along a straight line, and certainly not along the line plotted by MINITAB. So an exponential distribution is not a good fit for the recall times of either pleasant or unpleasant memories.

Solutions to Computer Exercises

Solution 1

This exercise covers some of the ideas and techniques discussed in Section 3 of *Unit A1* and in Chapter 3.

(a) The scatterplot is shown in Figure S.25.

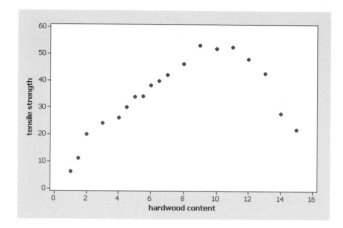

Figure S.25 Scatterplot of tensile strength and hardwood content for Kraft paper

(b) There appears to be a relationship between the percentage of hardwood in pulp and the strength of paper produced, but this relationship is not a linear one. When the percentage of hardwood is below 10% the paper strength appears to increase as the percentage of hardwood increases, but when the percentage is above 10% the strength decreases as the percentage of hardwood increases.

There are no obvious outliers in these data. The two rightmost points in Figure S.25 are certainly not close to any straight line that might be drawn through the rest of the data. However, there is clearly not a straight-line relationship between these two quantities, and the rightmost points arguably fit the falling pattern indicated by other points with high levels of hardwood content.

Solution 2

This exercise covers some of the ideas and techniques discussed in Section 1 of *Unit A2* and in Chapter 5.

(a) The boxplots in Figure S.26 can be obtained either using the data in the two columns, or after stacking the data in a single column, then editing the labels on the axes.

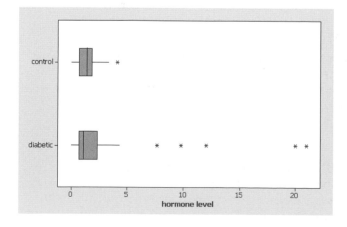

Figure S.26 Boxplots of (untransformed) fasting serum growth hormone levels

(b) The most obvious impression from the boxplots in Figure S.26 is that the level of the hormone can be much higher in diabetics than in others, because the boxplot for diabetics shows several potential high outliers. However, the 'box' parts of the boxplots are very squashed up towards the left of the diagram, so that it is hard to see much except the potential outliers. Since the data, certainly those for the diabetic patients, appear to be right-skew (long 'tails' to the right), a log transformation might reduce the skewness and make the comparison clearer. However, the hormone levels of two patients were recorded as 0.0 (see row 33 of diabetic and row 30 of control). MINITAB inserts a missing value symbol when the logarithm of 0 is calculated, and will not produce a boxplot for a column containing any missing values. One way of overcoming this problem is to replace 0.0 with a small value. Since the hormone levels are recorded to one decimal place, a value less than 0.05 should be used. If 0.0 is replaced by 0.025 (for instance), then boxplots of the data after transforming them by taking logarithms are as shown in Figure S.27.

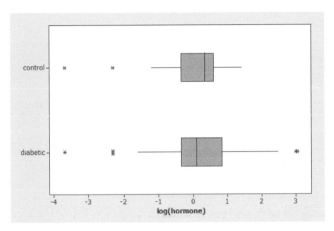

Figure S.27   Boxplots of transformed fasting serum growth hormone levels

The two points on the extreme left correspond to the patients whose levels were recorded as 0.0. The boxplot of the transformed data focuses on the main bulk of the data rather than on the outliers. Now it is easier to see that the general location of the hormone levels does not actually differ very much between the two groups of patients, but the spread is noticeably greater for the diabetic patients. It can be seen that this difference in spread is not confined to high hormone levels; the low levels are also more spread out for the diabetic patients.

Solution 3

This exercise covers some of the ideas and techniques discussed in Section 4 of *Unit A3* and in Chapter 8.

(a) Assuming that all passengers turn up (or not) independently of each other, it is reasonable to model the number of passengers who do not turn up by a binomial distribution: $X \sim B(140, 0.1)$.

(b) The number of standby passengers who get a seat on the flight is equal to the number of passengers out of the 140 with reservations that do not turn up for the flight. All the standby passengers will get a seat on the flight if at least 16 of the 140 passengers who have reserved seats do not turn up. So the probability required is

$$P(X \geq 16) = 1 - P(X \leq 15).$$

This probability may be found using **Binomial...** from the **Probability Distributions** submenu of the **Calc** menu. Select **Cumulative probability**, enter 140 and 0.1 for the parameters of the distribution, enter 15 in the **Input constant** field and click on **OK**. Then

$$P(X \geq 16) = 1 - P(X \leq 15) = 1 - 0.674802 = 0.325198 \simeq 0.3252.$$

(c) The probability that exactly half the standby passengers get seats on the flight is given by

$$P(X = 8) = 0.0272309 \simeq 0.0272.$$

Select **Probability** in the **Binomial Distribution** dialogue box and enter 8 in the **Input constant** field.

Solution 4

This exercise covers some of the ideas and techniques discussed in Sections 3 and 4 of *Unit A5* and in Chapters 12 and 13.

(a) If X is a random variable representing the number of major explosive volcanic eruptions that occur in a typical ten-year period, then X has a Poisson distribution with parameter

$$\lambda t = 0.0352 \times 120 = 4.224.$$

The probability required is

$$P(X > 5) = 1 - P(X \le 5) = 1 - F(5).$$

Choose **Poisson...** from the **Probability Distributions** submenu of the **Calc** menu. Enter the value 4.224 for the **Mean** in the **Poisson Distribution** dialogue box. Select **Cumulative probability** and enter 5 in the **Input constant** field. MINITAB returns the value 0.749214, so the probability required is

$$P(X > 5) = 1 - 0.749214 \simeq 0.2508.$$

(b) If T is a random variable representing the interval in months between successive major explosive volcanic eruptions, then T has an exponential distribution with parameter $\lambda = 0.0352$.

The mean interval between eruptions (in months) is $1/\lambda = 1/0.0352 \simeq 28.4$.

The probability required is $P(T < 6)$. Choose **Exponential...** from the **Probability Distributions** submenu and enter the value 28.4 in the **Scale** field in the **Exponential Distribution** dialogue box. Select **Cumulative probability** and enter 6 in the **Input constant** field.

According to MINITAB, the proportion of intervals that will be less than six months is

$$P(T < 6) = P(T \le 6) = F(6) = 0.190443 \simeq 0.1904.$$

(c) Since 5% of intervals are shorter than x months, x is the 0.05-quantile of the exponential distribution with mean 28.4; that is, $x = q_{0.05}$.

Choose **Exponential...** from the **Probability Distributions** submenu and enter the value 28.4 in the **Scale** field in the **Exponential Distribution** dialogue box. Select **Inverse cumulative probability** and enter 0.05 in the **Input constant** field.

The MINITAB output gives $x = 1.45673$. So only 5% of intervals are shorter than about $1\frac{1}{2}$ months.

(d) Since only 1% of intervals exceed y years, or $12y$ months, $12y$ is the 0.99-quantile of the exponential distribution with mean 28.4; that is, $12y = q_{0.99}$.

Proceed as in part (c), but enter 0.99 in the **Input constant** field.

The MINITAB output gives the value 130.787, so $12y = 130.787$. Hence $y = 130.787/12 \simeq 10.90$. So only 1% of intervals are longer than about 11 years.

Solution 5

This exercise covers some of the ideas and techniques discussed in *Unit A5* and in Chapters 12 and 14.

(a) If the waiting times are observations from an exponential distribution, then their mean and standard deviation should be approximately equal. The mean and standard deviation are 50.60 hours and 43.30 hours, respectively; so an exponential model is plausible.

These values were obtained using **Display Descriptive Statistics...** from the **Basic Statistics** submenu of the **Stat** menu.

Two of the waiting times were recorded as 0 (in rows 27 and 30). Since the data are given to the nearest half hour, these zeros correspond to intervals of less than a quarter of an hour. The exponential probability plot in Figure S.28 was obtained after replacing the two 0s by 0.2.

Instructions for obtaining an exponential probability plot are given in Computer Activities 14.2 and 14.3.

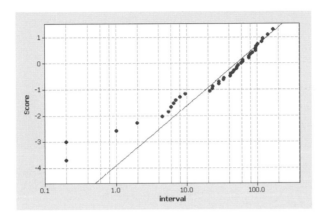

Figure S.28 An exponential probability plot for the waiting times between admissions

There are several points corresponding to very short intervals that are not close to the straight line. Since the remaining points are roughly along the line and fairly close to it, an exponential model for the waiting times between admissions is not totally implausible. However, there is reason to question the suitability of an exponential model.

(b) The function `Partial sum`, available when using **Calculator...** from the **Calc** menu, was used to obtain the partial sums of the waiting times. **Simple Set of Numbers...** from the **Make Patterned Data** submenu of the **Calc** menu was used to enter the numbers 1, 2, ..., 40 in a column called `number`. Figure S.29 shows a plot of the number of admissions so far against time.

See Computer Activity 12.1 for instructions on how to obtain such a plot.

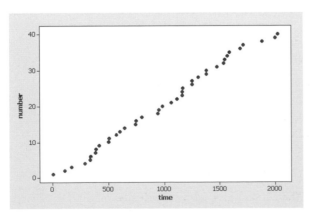

Figure S.29 A scatterplot for the admissions data

The points lie roughly along a straight line through the origin, suggesting that the average rate of admissions to the intensive care unit remained constant over the period to which the data relate. In fact, there are variations in the underlying rate of admission, both with the time of day and with the day of the week, which can be detected when the full set of the original data is analysed.

Index